WIMBLEDON PUBLISHING CON

LIBRARY OF QUALITY IN EDU

PHYSICS AND EARTH SCIENCE

By
Richard G R Balding
Summer Fields, Oxford

GENERAL EDITOR

K.S.Sood

B.Sc, M.Phil, A.R.C.S.

Wimbledon Publishing Company

ISBN 1 898855 08 0

Dedicated to the Very Highest Quality in Education

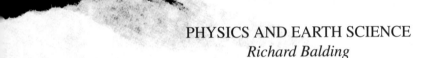

PHYSICS AND EARTH SCIENCE
Richard Balding

LIBRARY OF QUALITY IN EDUCATION

General Editor: K.S.Sood, B.Sc, M.Phil, ARCS

First Published in Great Britain in 1997 by
WIMBLEDON PUBLISHING COMPANY LIMITED
P.O.BOX 9779 London SW19 7ZG. Fax: +44 (0) 181 944 0825

ISBN 1 898855 08 0

Produced in Great Britain
Typesetting by GTI Graphics, London
Cover Design by Malvinder S.Soor, P.M. Graphics
Printed and bound in Hungary

FOR

The enjoyment and enrichment of life that a knowledge
of science provides.

DEDICATED TO

My numerous pupils, past, present and future

RICHARD G. R. BALDING

Richard Balding has had a distinguished teaching career. After a short career in industry, he decided early to teach young children and ever since he has excelled in his chosen career. He joined Summer Fields, Oxford, a leading well established preparatory school in England. In 1978 he was made the Head of the Science and Technology department at the school, a position that he still holds.

When time allows Richard is also interested in gardening and all forms of music. He sings in choirs (large ones!), and has played the clarinet in classical chamber ensembles and plays the saxophone in the successful dance band that he runs.

Richard is also deeply involved in the organisation of teaching of Science. He is currently IAPS Science coordinator, Chairman of Common Entrance Physics panel and has also edited the SATIP Technology broadsheet.

LIBRARY OF QUALITY IN EDUCATION

The basic premise of the Quality in Education series is to make available to teachers, pupils and their parents excellent resource material for the ultimate benefit of the pupils. The resource material in these books can be used to navigate the child to work from the average level to the outstanding level. The books are full of material which provide challenging exercises and enable the pupils to achieve 'horizontal' proficiency in learning, i.e. proficiency based on the level of knowledge that a pupil is expected to have, but extending the application of the knowledge to more challenging situations.

General Editor
September 1997

INTRODUCTION

TO THE STUDENT:

This book has been written to help you understand the basic principles and the main features of Physics and Earth Science. The material in this book covers all that you will need for your Key Stage 3 level as well as for the preparation for Common Entrance and 13 + Scholarship examinations to the Senior Independent Schools. It also provides a firm base for your first year of GCSE work.

There are two parts to each chapter; the **text** which sets out the material with which you are expected to be familiar with and some **questions** for you to answer and make sure that you have understood the principles.

The text is designed to be used at the ages of 13 and 14. Some previous knowledge of science is necessary if this book is to be used as a self help book. It may well be that you have missed some of the topics at some time during your Science Course, or there may have been some areas which you did not understand fully the basic principles involved and thus found your studies less rewarding than they might have been. This book is therefore also intended as a 'Gap Filler'.

Questions at the end of each chapter are divided into two sections. The first section entitled "WHAT DO YOU KNOW ABOUT ....?" helps you master the principles explained in the chapter. By fully answering these questions, you will help yourself to a firm foundation in the subject.

The second section entitled "FURTHER QUESTIONS...." are the more difficult questions. They test your ability to *apply* the principles and facts that you have learned and produce a clear, concise and well presented answer to problems. These questions are well suited to those taking the Scholarship examinations to the 13+ Independent sector. The questions in Scholarship Level papers are designed to test the ability to apply basic principles of science to solve problems which may at first appear unfamiliar or more complex. Some of the questions may not even have unique answers. They test the extent of your imagination. It is hoped that the questions in this section will provide you with practice at this level.

TO THE TEACHER:

This book covers material required to satisfy the requirements of the National Curriculum, Key Stage 3, Attainment Targets 2, 3, 4 and it is hoped that this book will be a useful addition to course material already used. The book is designed to help you in the following ways:
⇒ as a 'Check List' of the important topics which need to be covered at this stage;
⇒ as a **supply of questions** for reinforcement, assessment and homework purposes;
⇒ as a **source of revision material** prior to examinations;
⇒ as 'self help' material, which can be given to a student who is away from the laboratory for any length of time (say for illness, or for holiday work).

As this book is designed to help students increase their knowledge and understanding of the factual material required at this level, practical work (such as is detailed as Attainment Target 1) has not been included, even though it is a vital part of A Science Course. Any details of experiments and/or demonstrations have been included only as reinforcement of work which you may well have done in class time.

It is very important to realise that this book is an extension and an extra resource to compliment rather than replace existing materials which will, of course, include details of practical and investigative work.

ACKNOWLEDGEMENTS

I am most grateful to the support and encouragement which I have received from science colleagues who teach in a variety of schools, both Preparatory and Secondary. Their collective wisdoms and experiences will have contributed to this book, albeit, some of them unwittingly!

In particular, I would like to thank John Tucker, St Edward's School, Oxford and Gavin Hannah, Summer Fields, Oxford, who took the task of reading the manuscript prior to publication in an attempt to remove any 'howlers' that the Author was guilty of. Also thanks to Bill Bailey, Summer Fields, Oxford who made useful addition to the geographical content of some parts of the Earth Science section.

Mr K.S.Sood, Wimbledon Publishing Company, has been very patient and most helpful and the credit for turning a manuscript ramble into a coherent finished article belongs to him.

As most of this book has been produced at home I am thankful for the support and help which I have received here, especially from Polly and Anna who did some of the typing and Deborah who not only encouraged continuously, but remained understanding even as the whole house became submerged in paper.

Richard Balding

Summer Fields, Oxford.

January 1997.

Contents

PHYSICS, MATERIALS AND THEIR PROPERTIES

Whatever activity you take part in, you can be sure that you will be using physics!

If you are building a treehouse, you will need to use substances which are strong enough to carry your weight and yet light enough to be lifted into the tree. You might find that bare boards are too hard to sit on for a long time, so you will need to find something soft to sit on for comfort. You may even have to find a set of levers and pulleys to help you lift your materials into the tree.

In the classroom the electric lights, which enable you to do your work on dark evenings, are only possible because of the understanding of physics developed by former scientists such as Michael Faraday.

You will also know that to make your electric train work, good electrical connections have to be made. These connections also have to be the right way round, or else the train will go backwards!

In the kitchen you may well use metal saucepans with plastic, or wooden, handles and come to know that although plates made of china can be put to warm in the oven, plastic ones certainly cannot. You can **see** how much tomato ketchup there is left in a glass bottle, whereas some types of plastic containers will keep you guessing.

All the time, you are making decisions about which materials to use for a specific purpose. Although you may well be deciding 'without thinking', you are in fact *basing* your choice upon previous knowledge about each material which you have built up over the years.

States Of Matter

Look at the variety of materials around you and you will see that most of them can be put within three main groups: **SOLIDS, LIQUIDS** or **GASES.** These groups are known as the **States of Matter.**

Table 1: States of matter

SOLIDS	LIQUIDS	GASES
Fixed amount - mass	Fixed amount - mass	Fixed amount - mass
Fixed quantity - volume	Fixed quantity - volume	Changes volume
Fixed shape	Changes shape	Changes shape

> **Liquids** and **Gases** are called **FLUIDS** because they can change shape and flow

What Are Materials Made Of?

All substances are made up of tiny particles of matter called **ATOMS**. There are about 100 different types of atom and these join together to form **MOLECULES**.

Fig 1.1

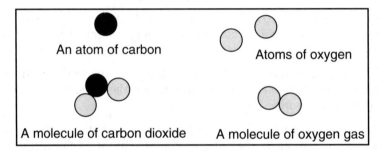

An atom of carbon

Atoms of oxygen

A molecule of carbon dioxide

A molecule of oxygen gas

All molecules have energy and are constantly moving. Sometimes this movement is from one place to another, as in fluids. At other times the movement takes the form of vibrations in one place, as in solids.

As molecules come really closer to each other, of the order of millionths of the thickness of hair, there are forces of attraction which 'bind' them together. There are various types of forces and methods of holding molecules together, but we shall group them together and call them the **'BINDING ENERGY'** of a substance.

It is important to realise that:

In **SOLIDS** the energy of the molecules is less than the 'Binding Energy' - so solids retain their shape.

In **LIQUIDS** the energy of the molecules is almost equal to the 'Binding Energy'.

In **GASES** the energy of the molecules is greater than the 'Binding Energy'- so the molecules are free to move, if they can.

How Do Substances Change State?

When we heat substances we add energy to them. This 'extra' energy is added to the energy of the already-moving molecules and so they go faster.

When we **cool** a substance, we **remove** energy from the molecules, which, now having less energy, slow down.

Let Us Look At Water

ICE (SOLID): The energy of the particles is **less** than the 'Binding Energy' so the molecules are 'held' in place with respect to each other. Thus the solid retains its shape.

WATER (LIQUID): The molecules have more energy and so move further apart. However, the amount of energy that each molecule has is **slightly less** than the 'Binding Energy' of water. This means that although they are free to change places with each other, and thus to alter the shape of the substance, most of the molecules do not have enough energy to 'break free'.

STEAM (GAS): Here the molecules have **more** energy than the 'Binding Energy' of water and are able to break free of the liquid. Because the molecules of a gas are free to roam, the gas will completely fill any container.

Melting Point / Boiling Point

The temperature at which the change **from solid to liquid** takes place is called the **Melting Point** (which in most cases is the same as the **Freezing Point,** the temperature at which the liquid changes to a solid).

The temperature at which the change from liquid to gas takes place is called the **Boiling Point.**

> **EACH SUBSTANCE** has its **OWN** Boiling Point* and Melting Point.

* This is true **only** at a given external pressure - often referred to as **'Standard Pressure'.**

Fig 1.2

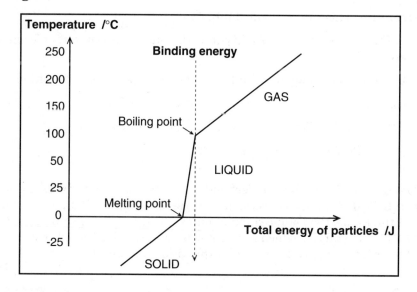

'Each Substance Has Its Own B.P. And M.P.' These are special to each substance and are used to identify the substance in its pure state. We can therefore call the B.P. or M.P. a **Property** of a substance and, in the case of B.P and M.P., these are more correctly called **PHYSICAL PROPERTIES**.

Fig 1.3 How molecules behave, as solids change into liquids and gases. gases

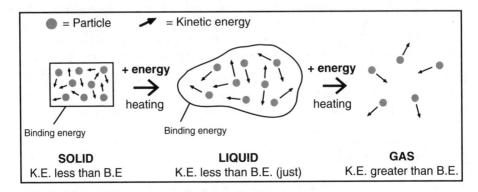

What Are Physical Properties?

These are properties which are special to substances and which may be observed and/or measured **without the substance changing into another substance.**

Physics is largely about the study of the physical properties of substances.

Apart from B.P./M.P., the **density** of a substance is another physical property which is used to identify a substance.

Some More Physical Properties

1. Strength: This can be divided into two types:

  a. Overall Strength - Ability to withstand loads without deforming or breaking.

  b. Tensile Strength - Ability to change shape without breaking.

  e.g.   *Flexibility:*   can be bent or twisted.

  Malleability: can be hammered into shape.

  Ductility :   can be drawn into wires.

2. Hardness: One of the simplest and most often used tests for hardness is a **Scratch Test**. If x makes a scratch on y, then x is harder than y. Diamond is one of the hardest substances found on earth. It is able to scratch and tear most other substances, which is why it is used in the tips (called **bits**) of drills used to drill through rocks as in oil exploration and mining.

3. Conductivity: Some materials will allow energy (thermal/electric) to pass through them;e.g. electricity passes through (is **CONDUCTED** by) wires which are usually made from metals such as copper. Materials which do not allow energy to pass through them are called **INSULATORS** - plastics are good insulators of energy, both thermal and electric.

4. Transparency: Some materials are completely see-through (**TRANSPARENT**) and let light pass through enabling you to see a clear image on the other side. Glass is a good example of a transparent material.

Some materials are **TRANSLUCENT**. This means that although they allow light to travel through them, you cannot see a clear image of what is on the other side. A sheet of tracing paper will do this.

Materials can be sorted into groups by examining their physical properties.

Main Groups Of Materials

Metals: Shiny, malleable, ductile, good conductors (thermal and electrical).

Ceramics: (*Made from baked clay.*) Hard, but brittle; good insulators of thermal and electrical energy; they can withstand high temperatures.

Glass: (*Made mainly from sand.*) Quite hard, but brittle; transparent or translucent; good insulator.

Fibres: (*Natural threads.*) Flexible, good insulators, soft.

Plastics: (*Made from chemicals - synthetic.*) Very flexible whilst hot; hence easy to mould. Some are flexible when cold; can be transparent or translucent or neither; good insulators.

What Do You Know About Materials?

1.   What are the differences between Solids, Liquids and Gases?

2.   What are fluids and why are they so called?

3.   Give three examples each of (i) a solid; (ii) a liquid; (iii) a gas.

4.   How many different types of atoms can you name? Stop at 20.

5.   What is a molecule?

6. A table of melting points and boiling points of some substances is given below.

	Melting Point/°C	Boiling Point/°C
A	97	890
B	39	357
C	0	100
D	220	180
E	117	78

(i) Represent this data in suitable graph/bar chart form.
(ii)Assuming that room temperature is 20°C
   (a) Which material/s is/are **solid** at room temperature?
   (b) Which material/s is/are **liquid** at room temperature?
   (c) Which material/s is/are **gas** at room temperature?

7. What does the term 'evaporate' mean?

8. What is meant by (i) The melting point; (ii) The boiling point of a substance?

9. Below is a list of fuels. Draw a table to show which are liquids and which are solids:
              coal, diesel, paraffin, peat, petrol, wood.

10. On a warm day, butter changes from solid to liquid. Describe the changes for the following examples:

Water boiling in a saucepan	from............to..........
Hot candle wax dripping onto the floor	from............to..........
Water vapour condensing on a cold window	from............to..........
Water turning to ice	from............to..........

11. Name an object which is
   a) part liquid, part gas;
   b) part solid, part gas;
   c) part solid, part liquid, part gas;
   d) part solid, part liquid.

12. Why are nails made from iron rather than lead?

13. Bottles are now made from plastic instead of glass. Give two **advantages** and two **disadvantages** of this.

14. Plastic saucepans are not a good idea - why?

Further Questions On Materials

1. Oxygen and nitrogen are extracted from the air by cooling the gases (at high pressure) until they become liquid. The boiling point of nitrogen is **-196 °C** and the boiling point of oxygen is **-183 °C**.
    i) when the air is cooled, which of the two gases changes to liquid first ?
    ii) how cold must the air be for nitrogen to have just changed to liquid ?
    iii)how cold must the air be for both gases to have changed to liquid?

2. Explain, in terms of molecules, what the three states of matter are and how it is that a substance can exist in all three states.

3. You have invented a new material with the following properties:
    - it is an electrical conductor
    - it is a poor conductor of thermal energy
    - it glows in the dark
    - it has a very low density
    - it is tough in large lumps, but can also be made in thin sheets, when it is like rubber.
    Suggest, with reasons, some possible uses for this new material.

4. What do you understand by the terms below which describe physical properties? Give examples to support your answers.
    i) hardness
    ii) translucence
    iii) conductivity
    iv) strength (general and tensile)

5. At some hotels, drinks by the poolside are often served in plastic 'glasses'. Why is this a good idea?

6. When ice melts, what happens to the molecules and why?

7. The electric cable to a vacuum cleaner contains three separate wires, each having a different colour (brown, blue, green/yellow).
    Make a labelled drawing of such a cable and say what materials will be used in it and why.

8. The modern soldier wears a combat kit made from fibre. A soldier from the Middle Ages may well have worn a suit of armour made from metal. Considering the physical properties of the two types of material used, discuss the differences in comfort and effectiveness of the two soldiers from different periods.

9. A Stone Age axe would have been very sharp when it was made. This being so, why was it an improvement when, subsequently, axes came to be made from iron?

2   MEASUREMENTS AND UNITS

When a fisherman tells you how big the fish was that he caught, do you believe him?

An Eskimo landing at London Airport may well find the air temperature very hot, whereas we may think it is a cold day!

A pilot has to know exactly how high he is on the approach to the runway for landing. He also needs to know how fast the aircraft is flying, as well as the strength and direction of the wind blowing across the airfield. He will have instruments in the aircraft to help him and he will rely upon accurate measurements being made by people on the ground, which will be radioed to him from the control tower.

When making a box in the workshop, it is important that some pieces are exactly the same size.

The wheels on a buggy that you are making need to be exactly the same size if the buggy is to run smoothly!

If your body temperature varies by a few degrees then you may well feel poorly.

There is hardly any activity in our everyday lives which does not require measurement of some sort or another. Certainly you will have made many measurements during your science course.

Measurements set a common language for everyone to understand. If your travel-bag has a mass of 15kg, then this will be understood by airline officials at airports all over the world. It is not enough merely to say that it is not very heavy. They will need a measurement in order to find out how much luggage can be carried safely in the aeroplane.

Are Units Important?

In a word, YES!

Remember that there are always **two** parts to a measurement - a **number** and a **unit**. The **number** tells you the **amount** of what you have measured. The **unit** describes **what it is** that you have been measuring.

10 on its own is meaningless. 10 what? 10 grammes, 10 apples, 10 metres?

These are all different and it is the **UNIT**, usually expressed as an abbreviation, which is required to tell you what it is you have 10 of.

What Is Measured	Unit Name	Abbreviation
Mass	Kilogram	kg
Length	Metre	m
Time	Second	s
Energy	Joule	J*
Force	Newton	N*
Electric current	Ampere	A*

*These units use Capital Letters because they are named after the famous scientists associated with them.

The abbreviation is both singular **and** plural, e.g. 1 A, 2 A, 50 A etc.

Never add an s̲ to make a unit plural (as in 2As), for s̲ is the unit of time; **the second**.

Powers Of Ten And Standard Form

We could say that the diameter of Saturn is 120,000 km. This is a very clumsy way of writing such a large number and could well lead to errors! It is much simpler to express big numbers using **Standard Form**. In this case the diameter of Saturn can be expressed as 1.2×10^5km which is much simpler.

12 is 1.2×10 or, in Standard Form, 1.2×10^1

120 is $1.2 \times 10 \times 10$ or, in Standard Form, 1.2×10^2

1 200 is $1.2 \times 10 \times 10 \times 10$ or, in Standard Form, 1.2×10^3

12 000 is $1.2 \times 10 \times 10 \times 10 \times 10$ or, in Standard Form, 1.2×10^4

120 000 is $1.2 \times 10 \times 10 \times 10 \times 10 \times 10$ or, in Standard Form, 1.2×10^5

Points To Remember

(a) It is usual in Standard Form to have **ONE** figure either side of the decimal point. (Some 'rounding up or down' may be needed.)

(b) 000 s are now separated by a **space** rather than a comma.

(c) The 'rules' for multiplying and dividing indices apply:

e.g. $(2.5 \times 10^7) \times (2 \times 10^6) = 5.0 \times 10^{13}$

Measuring Length

The Standard Unit is the Metre (m). However, this is not a convenient unit for measuring the diameter of Saturn. So we use kilometres (km).

For small distances, such as the length of a pencil, we use centimeters (cm) or millimetres (mm).

The table below summarises the information.

Unit	Multiple/Fraction of the Standard Unit	Unit Expressed in Standard Form
Kilometre(km)	1000m	1.0×10^3
METRE	STANDARD UNIT	
Centimetre	1/100m or 0.01m	1.0×10^2
Millimetre	1/1000m or 0.001m	1.0×10^3

The **prefixes** give the clue:

    kilo   –   is the Standard Unit × 1000 '-o-' for multiplying
    centi –   is the Standard Unit ÷ 100 '-i-' for dividing
    milli   –   is the Standard Unit ÷ 1000
    (Clearly 10 millimetres = 1 centimetre).

Measuring Area

Area is the size of a flat surface and is measured in square metres (m^2).
(a) The area of the *whole frame* is : 3 m × 6 m = 18 m^2.
(b) The area of the *shaded part* is : 7 whole squares + 4 squares (more than half shaded) = 11m^2 approx.

The accuracy of (b) will of course be increased by reducing the size of the square.

Fig 2.1 Measuring Areas Of Irregular Figures

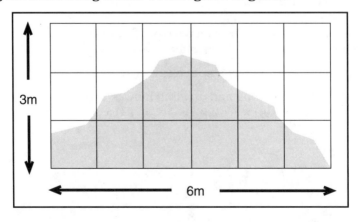

Measuring Volumes

In simple terms, volume tells us HOW BIG a solid object is. In the case of liquid, it tells us HOW MUCH LIQUID we have. In the laboratory, it is usual to measure volumes in cubic centimetres (cm³).

Volume Of Liquids:

Liquids are sometimes measured in litres (l) or millilitres (ml) and you may well have come across measuring cylinders marked in *ml*. However, as there is such a tiny difference between the volume of 1 litre and 1000 cm³ of water, it is perfectly satisfactory and usual to measure both solids and liquids in cm³. It is usual to measure the volume of liquids in the laboratory by using a **measuring cylinder**.

Fig 2.2 Using a measuring cylinder

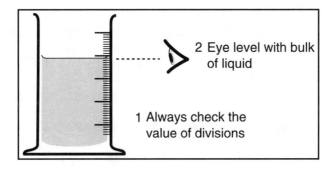

Fig 2.3 Reading a measuring cylinder

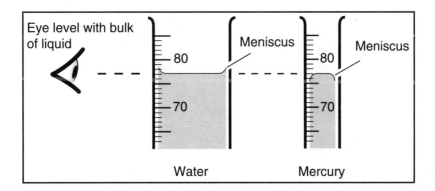

Volume Of Solids:

(i) Regular Shaped Solids

Simply measure the Length (l_1), width (l_2) and height (l_3) and multiply them together.

Fig 2.4 Volume = $l_1 \times l_2 \times l_3$ cm^3

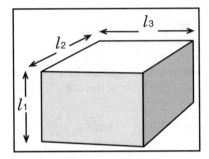

(ii) Irregular - Shaped Solids.

As a liquid and solid cannot both occupy the same space, we use the fact that a non-porous solid will push away (displace) water. The amount of water which is displaced will be the same as the size (volume) of the object which is put into the liquid.

(a) Using a measuring cylinder

Fig 2.5   Vol. of object = 'New Vol.' – 'Old Vol'

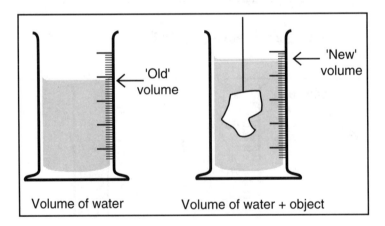

(b)   Using a Displacement ('EUREKA')* Can

> * Named after Archimedes and quoting his famous 'cry of joy' when he discovered a method for finding the volume of irregular shaped objects.

Fig 2.6 Volume of object = volume of overflow

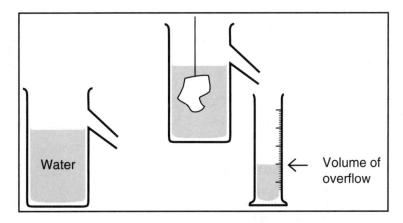

Volumes Of Gases

Fig 2.7 A gas syringe:

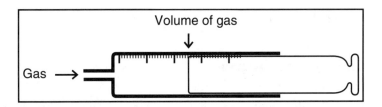

Because gases have no fixed shape, but will completely fill any container, we measure the **size of the container** which they are in. This could be a measuring cylinder (inverted over water) or, more usually, a gas syringe, like the one shown in the diagram above.

Measuring Mass

This is done by placing objects on scales and reading off the mass in kg (or grams).

Sadly there is no verb 'to mass' so we call the activity weighing. What we are really finding is the amount of material present in the object.

Old-fashioned balances used the principle of **comparing masses** to find the mass of an object. These sorts of balances are very similar to the Chemical Balances which you may have in your laboratory.

Nowadays these have tended to be replaced by top-loading balances - which are rather like kitchen scales and which may be electronically operated.

Fig 2.8. A Chemical Balance.

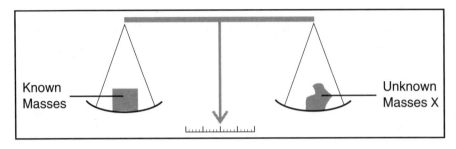

When the scales balance, the mass of X = the sum of the known masses

So Is Weight The Same As Mass?

What is the confusion between Mass and Weight? There should not be any because they are two entirely different things.

MASS is the **amount of material** in a body and measured in kilogrammes.

WEIGHT is the **force** which a whole body exerts because it is pulled downwards (towards the Earth's centre) by the invisible force which we call gravity. Weight is measured in Newtons (N).

It is vital to be able to distinguish between the two.

Measuring Temperatures

The only way to decide exactly how hot a cup of tea is, is to take the temperature by using a thermometer. We have already seen that at higher temperatures, molecules circulate more freely. In doing so they <u>create</u> more room to move about. So, the solid, liquid or gas tries to become larger, i.e. it expands. As liquids expand more than solids, so the liquid thermometer works on the principle of expansion of a liquid. In laboratory thermometers the most usual liquid used is mercury, although you may well have come across thermometers which use alcohol. However, as alcohol has a boiling point of 78 °C, which is much less than water (100 °C), then this makes its use in the laboratory rather restrictive. Alcohol is, however, often employed in thermometers which are used to record the temperature of the air as part of weather reading.

The scale most used in the laboratory at this stage, is the CELSIUS scale and we talk about 'degrees C' or °C.

How Was The Celsius Scale Arrived At?

Quite simply an unmarked thermometer was put into some melting ice for some time, and a scratch was made at the top of the mercury column. This was called 0 ˚C. Then the *same* thermometer was put into some steam and another scratch was made, at the new top of the mercury column. This was called 100 ˚C. The distance between the two scratches was divided into 100 equal steps (or Centigrades - hence the original term 'Centigrade'). Nowadays, the scale is named after Anders Celsius who discovered it in 1742.

Fig. 2.9. A Mercury Thermometer

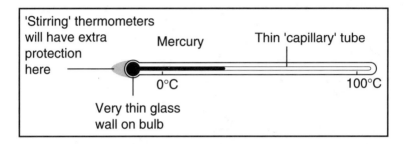

Notice that the glass wall of the bulb where the mercury is stored is very thin. This is to enable the energy from whatever is being measured to be conducted to the mercury as quickly as possible.

Equally, when the thermometer is removed from hot liquid, or whatever, the mercury level falls as the bulb cools down.

Imagine this design of thermometer being used to take your body temperature. When the thermometer is removed from under your tongue into the colder air, the mercury will contract and the level will start to fall. Not a help to the person trying to read the scale and determine how ill you are!

In order to overcome this problem, clinical thermometers which take your body temperature, have a constriction in the tube just above the bulb which allows mercury to flow into the area where the readings are, but **not** back into the bulb. In fact, the mercury can be returned to the bulb by shaking, once the temperature has been recorded.

Fig 2.10. A Clinical Thermometer

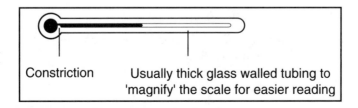

Celsius or Fahrehnheit?

Sometimes on weather maps you will see 20°C (68°F). Both figures represent the same air temperature, but they are measured using different scales.

Melting Point Of Ice		Boiling Point Of Water	
Celsius Scale	0°C	100 divisions	100°C
Fahrenheit Scale	32°F	180 divisions	212°F

How Do We Change From One Scale To The Other?

You will have noticed that 180 divisions on the Fahrenheight Scale correspond to 100 divisions of the Celsius Scale.

Thus we can express this as the ratio

$$\frac{180}{100} = \frac{°F}{°C}$$

or, simplifying,

$$\frac{9}{5} = \frac{°F}{°C}$$

So,

$$9°C = 5°F$$

So,

$$°C = \frac{5}{9}°F$$

Simple, but not the full story, because when °C = 0, °F = 32!

So to make our relationship, $°C = \frac{5}{9}°F$ work when °C = 0, we need to subtract 32 from the value of F.

This gives

$$C = \frac{5}{9}(F - 32)$$

Now it will work when C = 0.

We have

$$0 = \frac{5}{9}(32 - 32)$$

So,

$$0 = \frac{5}{9}(0)$$

Thus

$$0 = 0$$

This confirms that the relationship (called a **formula**) enabling us to convert temperatures in Fahrenheit into °C is

$$°C = \frac{5}{9}(°F - 32)$$

Changing From Celsius To Fahrenheit

e.g. *What is 20 °C in °F?*

Start with the relationship, $°C = \frac{5}{9} \, (°F - 32)$

Rearrange it to make F the subject (if in doubt, *always* do this step by step).

Thus, $\qquad °C \times \frac{9}{5} \; = \; °F - 32$

So, $\qquad\qquad °F \; = (°C \times \frac{9}{5}) + 32$

Put in the figures (20 °C).

So, $\qquad °F \; = (20 \times \frac{9}{5}) + 32$

So, $\qquad °F \; = (36) + 32$

So $\qquad\; °F \; = 68$

Nowadays, as temperatures for laboratory work are nearly always given as °C, you will not often need to convert from one scale to the other. You certainly do not need to REMEMBER the conversion formula but, having been given it, you should be able to follow the stages above and rearrange it to enable you to convert temperatures from one scale to another.

After all, one of the important skills which you need to acquire, is how to handle confidently the measurements which you have made. This is where your study of mathematics is very closely tied up with your studies in physics. The measuring is the physics part and the handling of measurements, in such a way as to provide the answers to problems, is the mathematical part. You need **both** parts to achieve a satisfactory whole.

The Kelvin Scale

The coldest possible temperature is -273 °C and this is called **Absolute Zero**.

The Kelvin scale begins at absolute zero, but increases just like the Celsius scale.

Thus: $\qquad$ -273 °C $\qquad$ becomes 0 Kelvin (written 0 K). Do **NOT** write °K

$\qquad\qquad\quad$ 0 °C $\qquad$ becomes 273 Kelvin (written 273 K)

So:

Temperature in Kelvin = °C + 273

What Do You Know About Measurement?

1. List **ten** everyday examples where measurement is required.

2. What would you use to measure the following?
    (i) The amount of ink in your ink bottle.
    (ii) The height of a Bunsen burner.
    (iii)How hot a beaker of water is.
    (iv)The mass of an apple.
    (v) The length of a cricket pitch.

3. For **each** of the parts of Q2, say which units you would use.

4. How many cm are there in
    1m, 1.8m, 3.6 km, 0.8 m?

5. What is the area (in cm^2) of the following?
    (i) A square of sides 3 cm.
    (ii) A square of sides 1m.
    (iii)A rectangle measuring 5 cm by 77 cm.
    (iv)A rectangle measuring 50 cm by 7 m.
    (v) A rectangle measuring 50 m by 700m.

6. Express your answers to Q5 parts (iv) and (v) in Standard Form.

7. How many cm^3 are there in m^3 ?
    Write down your answer in:
    (i) words;
    (ii) figures;
    (iii)standard form.

8. How many boxes of pins, each measuring 2 cm × 3 cm × 0.5 cm, can you
    fit into a box measuring 60 cm × 30 cm × 15 cm?

9. You have a carton which is half full of milk. You have access to any
    equipment in the laboratory.
    How would you:

    (i)   Find the volume of the milk?

    (ii) Find the mass of the milk?

10. Draw a series of labelled diagrams to show how you would measure the
    volume of a penknife using a displacement (Eureka) can.

11. How would you measure the thickness of ONE page of this book?

12. You have a box containing about 500 marbles which are all similar. Each
    one has a diameter of about 0.5 cm.
    (i) How would you measure the diameter of ONE marble as accurately
    as possible?
    (ii) How would you find the mass of ONE marble as accurately as possible?

Further Questions On Measurements And Units

1. The distance from the Earth to the Sun is 93,000,000 miles (150,000,000 km).
    (i) Write down both of these distances in Standard Form.
    (ii) How many kilometres are there in 1 mile?

2. A new hotel is to be built. It will be 50 floors high, each floor being 3 m high. All the rooms are around the outside of the building and the shape of the building is a square, with 5 rooms on each side. Each room is 6 m wide.
    (a) What will be the height of the new hotel?
    (b) How many rooms could there be?
    (c) Is your answer to (b) likely? If not, explain why.
    (d) If all the sides of the hotel are covered in glass, what area of glass is required?
    (e) You need to make an architect's model of the hotel, using card, to a scale of 1 : 100.
    (i) How tall will your model be?
    (ii) What will be the area of the base of your model?
    (iii)Write down the area of card that you would use. Show your reasoning.

3. Copy the table below and write, in the spaces provided, examples with roughly the masses or lengths indicated.

Masses		Lengths	
Mass	Example	Length	Example
1kg	A bag of sugar	1m	height of lab table
100kg		100m	
0.1kg		0.1m	
0.001kg		0.001m	

4. An atom of carbon can be thought of as a cube with each side 2×10^{-10} m.
    (a) (i) What is the volume of a carbon atom (in m^3)?
    (ii) What is the volume (in m^3) of a pencil lead 0.8 mm thick and 5 cm long?
    [$\pi = 3$ take as vol of a cylinder = $\pi r^2 h$]
    (iii) Assuming that the lead is made of carbon, how many carbon atoms are there in the pencil lead from Q4 (a)(ii)?

(b) An Electron microscope can magnify by a factor of 10 million and display the results on a screen measuring 20cm by 20cm.
(i) How many carbon atom images will be seen along ONE SIDE of the screen?
(ii)How many carbon atom images will be seen on the ENTIRE screen?

5.　(a) Using the relationship $°C = \frac{5}{9} (°F - 32)$, convert the following temperatures to °C:
(i) 212 °F　　(ii) 77 °F　　　　(iii) 140 °F　　　　(iv) 23 °F

(b) Rearrange the relationship $°C = \frac{5}{9} (°F - 32)$ and convert the following temperatures to °F:

(i) 0 °C　　(ii) 50 °C　　　　(iii) –10 °C　　　　(iv) 75 °C

6.　What do the following Celsius temperatures become in Kelvin?

(i) 10 °C　　(ii) –198 °C　　　(iii)　37 °C

7.　You have found an old thermometer with all the markings rubbed off. You have access to all the usual laboratory equipment, including ice from the fridge. You have with you marking pens, ruler, calculator and rubber bands.

You are required to measure the temperature of some water which has been standing in a beaker on a laboratory side bench for about six hours.

Describe what you would do and what measurements you would make in order to find the temperature of the water in the beaker.

THE DENSITY OF SUBSTANCES
An Important Concept

We have to be careful how we use the word 'heavy'. It is not **always** true to say that iron is heavier than wood. Nails are made from iron and you will know that a nail is much easier to carry than a plank of wood. So you could argue, in an 'Alice in Wonderland' way, that wood is heavier than iron!

Clearly this is nonsense and in order to be able to say that material A is heavier than material B, we have to compare the masses of **EQUAL AMOUNTS** of A and B.

From your geographical studies, you will know that the population of London is said to be DENSER than the population of a similar sized area of the Scottish Highlands. The number of people living per square kilometre in each area will have been counted and the resulting number is called the **Population Density.**

Also, if a jungle is called a **DENSE** jungle, then the trees and various plants are growing so closely together, that it is difficult to move through.

So it is with materials.

Each and every substance has its own special number called its **DENSITY**, which describes how much matter is packed **into a specified quantity of it**. The specified quantity is usually 1m³.

The **AMOUNT** of matter in a given quantity of material is its **MASS** measured in kg. The **AMOUNT OF SPACE** which the material occupies is its **VOLUME** - measured in m³.

So,

> The Density of a material is the **mass** (number of grammes) for **each** m³.
>
> **The unit of density is kg/m³.**

In your laboratory work, you will probably have measured mass in *g* and volume in *cm³*. This is fine, and we shall express density as:

> **The mass (number of grammes) per each cm³ OR g/ cm³ .**

We shall use this as the unit of density for the rest of this book.

A Further Look At The Unit of Density

Density is a **COMPOUND** unit because it contains **two** quantities, mass and volume, which are combined by the use of '*/*'.

'*/*' in words, means '*per*' or '*for each*', or '*in each*', or '*is divided by*'.

Thus, the unit of density can be expressed in words as:
The number of grammes of matter *per cm³*;
The number of grammes of matter *for each cm³* ;
The number of grammes of matter *in each cm³*;
The number of grammes of matter *divided by the number of cm³*.

The UNIT tells us **how** to find the density of any amount of material, for, as you know, material does not always come in handy 1cm³ cubes!
g is the number of grammes of material i.e. the MASS of the material.
cm³ is the quantity/amount of the material i.e. the VOLUME of the material.
Thus:

$$\text{Density(g/cm}^3) = \frac{\text{TOTAL MASS of material(g)}}{\text{TOTAL VOLUME of material(cm}^3)}$$

Or,   where   D = density, M = mass, V = volume,

$$D = \frac{M}{V}$$

You will see that the unit (g/cm³) is the same **both** sides of the '=' sign.

'=' means '*is equal to*' and needs to be used with care!

Statements which contain the '=' sign are known as **EQUATIONS** and are used when everything on the left hand side of the '=' sign is **exactly the same** as everything on the right hand side. You will know all about the rules for dealing with equations from your studies in maths!

So, if you remember the UNIT of density as g/cm³, you will **always** arrive at the equation $D = \dfrac{M}{V}$ the correct way round.

[Just as if you remember that speed is measured in miles or kilometres (Distance) per hour (Time), you will always arrive at $S = \dfrac{D}{T}$ and not have to resort to memory gadgets!]

The whole point is that you should **know what the units are** for the quantity which you are measuring. In that way, your study of physics will have much greater meaning, because you will understand each step as you carry out your investigations.

If you merely rote-learn a collection of equations and try to put a suitable one into the appropriate slot to solve a problem, you may well find the answers to numerical problems, but your understanding of physics may well be superficial and could lead to unnecessary problems later on.

> **Work Step – by – Step and always be careful how you use Units.**

Of course physicists use equations. They will also use their mathematical skills to change equations around when needed, but they will **always** be careful to know and understand the units they use.

Now back to the Nails and Wood.

Remember, we are trying to find out which is the heavier of the two and to **really** understand what we mean by the word 'heavy'.
The wood measures 200 cm × 10 cm × 3 cm and has a mass of 3.6 kg.
The nail has a volume of 2 cm³ and has a mass of 15.8 g.

Looking at the Wood:

1) *Set the Scene*: Volume of wood is 200 cm × 10 cm × 3 cm = 6000 cm³
   Mass of wood is   3.6 × 1000 g = 3 600 g

2) *Write the equation:* $\text{Density} = \dfrac{\text{Mass}}{\text{Volume}}$

3) *Put in the figures:* $\text{Density} = \dfrac{3\ 600\ \text{g}}{6\ 000\ \text{cm}^3}$

4) *Cancel down / simplify*: $\text{Density} = \dfrac{6\ \text{g}}{10\ \text{cm}^3}$

5) *Calculate*: $\text{Density} = \dfrac{0.6\ \text{g}}{\text{cm}^3}$

6) *Make a statement*:   "The density of the wood is 0.6 g cm⁻³."

Looking at the nail:

1) *Set the "Scene"*:   Volume of nail = 2 cm³
   Mass of nail   = 15.8 g

2) *Write the equation*: $\text{Density} = \dfrac{\text{Mass}}{\text{Volume}}$

3) *Put in the figures*:   Density = 15.8 g ÷ 2 cm³
4) *Calculate*:   Density = 7.9 g ÷ cm³
5) *Make a statement*:   "The density of the nail is 7.9 g cm⁻³".

Now it becomes clear that in physics, when we talk about something being 'heavier' we actually mean that it is **more dense.** In our case, the nail has a greater density than the wood.

Turning It All Around

Say we need to find the **mass** of a known volume of material whose density is known. How do we do it?

There are two ways:
Method 1) by rearranging the Density Equation - a useful technique to master.

Method 2) by using the 'Density Statement' and Unitary Method.
It will be much clearer if we use some figures, so let us take a specific problem.

What is the mass of a 10 cm³ block of aluminium which has a density of 2.7 g/ cm³?

Method 1: rearranging the Density Equation:
We want to find an expression in which M = something i.e.make M the

*'subject'*of the formula given that $D = \dfrac{M}{V}$.

To **remove V** from the expression $\dfrac{M}{V}$, we need to **multiply by V**

Thus, $\dfrac{M \times V}{V}$ will cancel down to $\dfrac{M \times 1}{1}$ or just M.

So, in our equation, we multiply **both** sides by V, giving:

$$D \times V = \frac{M \times V}{V}$$

Simplifying/cancelling down: $D \times V = M$ or $M = D \times V$.

1) *Set the scene:* $D = 2.7 \text{g/cm}^3$, $V = 10 \text{ cm}^3$, M = ?
2) *Write the equation:* $M = D \times V$
3) *Put in the figures*: $M = 2.7 \text{gcm}^{-3} \times 10 \text{ cm}^3$
4) *Calculate* [note that the cm³ s cancel]: M = 27 g
5) *Write a statement:* "A 10 cm³ block of aluminium has a mass of 27 g."

Method 2: Using the Density Statement

What is meant by the 'Density Statement'?

This can be expressed in **two** ways.
As aluminium has a density of 2.7 g/cm³, we can say

either   **(A):**   2.7 g of aluminium has a volume of 1 cm³
or   **(B):**   1 cm³ of aluminium has a mass of 2.7 g.

> We use statement **A** if we want to find the **Volume** of a specified mass of a substance.
>
> We use statement **B** if we want to find the **Mass** of a specified mass of a substance.

In this case, we want to find the Mass, so we use statement B.

Find the volume for 1 cm³: 130 cm³ of aluminium has a mass of 2.7 g.

Multiply by the specified quantity: So, 10 cm³ of aluminium has a mass of 2.7 g × 10 = 27 g

Write a statement: "A 10 cm³ block of aluminium has a mass of 27 g."

Handy Hints On Solving Numerical Problems In Physics

If you wish to find the answers to a whole range of questions about objects and materials, then having made the appropriate measurements, you need to be able to **use** the figures to provide the solution to a particular question.

Handling numerical data confidently is an important skill which you should acquire, so we shall have a close look at how you can achieve this.

Although we have worked through an example using two different methods, there is a fundamental sequence which you should follow and, as has been said before, it is vital to work **STEP BY STEP** even though it may be tempting to miss out some of the steps in what may appear to be 'easy' problems.

If you follow the sequence, as we did in the previous examples, you will get into the habit of working carefully and then be able to tackle more complex problems with greater confidence and competence.

The general sequence for all types of problems is given below.

Stage I: 'SET THE SCENE'. Write down all the information (data) which you are given and what you are trying to find out. You may well include a simple diagram - but make sure that you include in the diagram **all** relevant figures and units.

Stage II: SHOW HOW YOU ARE GOING TO SOLVE THE PROBLEM. Write down any equation which you are going to use.

Stage III: REARRANGE THE EQUATION (if necessary).

Stage IV: PUT IN THE FIGURES WITH UNITS.

Stage V: SIMPLIFY BY CANCELLING DOWN THE FIGURES (AND UNITS).

Stage VI: DO THE CALCULATION TO OBTAIN A NUMERICAL ANSWER.

Stage VII: WRITE AN ANSWER. This is often forgotten and is a useful way of checking whether or not you have really solved the problem. It is also useful to check if your answer is a sensible one in the context i.e. if you were asked to find the mass of something have you answered in g?

The above sequence may look as if you are trying to 'push in a drawing pin with a sledgehammer' but there are, obviously, occasions when you will not need to use all the stages.

> **Nevertheless, it is important to work through all problems**
> **Step–by–Step.**

New Question: *If a 10 cm³ block of aluminium has a mass of 10 g and a density of 2.7 g/cm³, what would be the density of a block 20 times bigger?*

Let us look at the figures first.

The nail is 20 times bigger, so we first multiply the mass and volume by 20.

Thus, M = 27 g × 20, V = 10 cm³ × 20 = 540 g = 200 cm³

$$D = \frac{M}{V}$$

$$= \frac{540\ g}{200\ cm^3}$$

$$= 2.7\ gcm^{-3}$$

So the answer is that although the mass and volume of a particular substance may change, the **DENSITY REMAINS THE SAME, provided that the temperature remains the same**.

This means that both the smallest and largest piece of aluminium will have a density of 2.7 g/cm³.

The density of a substance is a **PHYSICAL PROPERTY** (in the same way that Melting and Boiling Points are physical properties - see chapter 1) and is a way of identifying it.

Why does the temperature have to remain the same?

You will remember that all materials are made from particles which are constantly moving and that adding energy (by heating) causes the molecules to move about more vigorously.

As this happens, they move **further apart** so the substance becomes larger **(EXPANDS)**.

Solids do not expand as much as liquids and gases but, even so, there **is** an increase in size (volume). We have already seen this in liquids when we saw how liquid thermometers work. In the case of a mercury thermometer, as the temperature rises, the volume of the mercury increases, but there is **NO** change in the mass of the mercury.

If you look at the equation **Density = $\dfrac{\textbf{Mass}}{\textbf{Volume}}$** , then you can see that as you increase the volume, keeping the mass the same, the **density will decrease**.

This is why it is important to say that the density of a substance does not change provided that the temperature remains the same.

Now you should be able to explain the physics ideas behind the saying 'Hot air rises'!

Density Of Liquids

It is easy to find the volume of a liquid in the laboratory, as you merely pour the liquid into a measuring cylinder and read off the volume using the graduations marked on the side of the cylinder.

Finding the **mass** is a little more complex, as liquids are **NEVER** poured into measuring cylinders **whilst they are standing on scales.**

To find the Mass of a liquid:

1) Weigh an empty measuring cylinder - call it **C** g

2) Take the measuring cylinder off the scales and pour in the liquid.

3) Weigh the measuring cylinder + liquid - call it (**C + L**) g

4) MASS OF LIQUID = (**C + L**) g – **C** g

       = **L** g

Having found the mass and volume of the liquid, you are now in a position to calculate its density.

Densities Of Some Liquids

Water	1.0 g/cm³
Methylated spirit	0.8 g/cm³
Mercury	13.6 g/cm³

You are not expected to remember the density of substances, but as you progress through your physics course, you will use the densities of water and mercury so many times that you will remember them!

Floating And Sinking

Example I: A block of wood (density 0.6 g/cm³) will float on water (density 1.0 g/cm³), whereas a block of aluminium (density 2.7 g/cm³) will sink.

Example II: A block of lead (density 11.3 g/cm³) will float on mercury (density 13.6 g/cm³), whereas a block of gold (density 19.3 g/cm³) will sink.

From these two examples, you can see that if the density of the block is **less** than the density of the liquid, it will **float** and if the density of the block is **more** than the density of the liquid, then it will **sink.**

Likewise, water (density 1.0 g/cm³) will float on mercury (density 13.6 g/cm³) but will sink in methylated spirits (density 0.8 g/cm³). You may well have seen this demonstrated for you.

Why Do Some Substances Float?

Fig 3.1

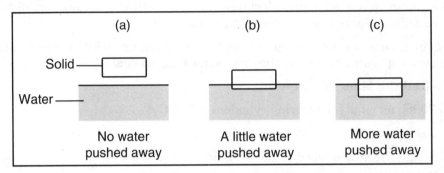

It was Archimedes who discovered that the amount of water 'pushed away'(displaced), by an object was the same as the volume of the object immersed in the water. The 'displaced' water pushes at the object being immersed - this is call the **upthrust**.

Upthrust is a 'push'. The water exerts an upward push on the object.
Clearly, in our diagram, the upthrust in (c) is greater than the upthrust in (b). The object will also be pulled downwards by the Earth's gravity. This pull downwards is what we call **weight**.

> **If upthrust is greater than the weight of the object, the object will float.**

More of this later, but by now you will begin to realise that the weight of an object depends upon its mass, and that the volume of the object immersed in a liquid is related to the upthrust by the liquid.

The connection between the **mass** and **submerged volume** of both the **object and liquid** is, of course, the **densities** of the object and liquid.

Density Of Gases

Gases are generally invisible and have such little mass that we sometimes find it hard to believe that they would have a density.

However, we know that carbon dioxide will sink in air, whereas a balloon filled with hydrogen will float upwards.

So, as we have already seen with floating and sinking in solids and liquids, carbon dioxide is **more** dense and hydrogen is **less** dense than air.

Finding The Density Of Gases

1) Density Of Oxygen: When potassium permanganate is heated, it decomposes to form a solid residue and the gas oxygen as described by the word equation;

> **Potassium Permanganate(VII)   Heating   Solid Residue + Oxygen**

It is a fundamental idea in chemistry that:

> Total mass at the start   =   Total mass at the end of
> of a reaction   a reaction

So, the **mass** of oxygen = (mass of potassium permanganate(VII) minus the mass of residue).

The oxygen released during the reaction can be collected in a gas syringe and its **volume** measured directly.

Let us take an actual example.

Remember, because gases expand with a rise in temperature, it is important to allow the **whole apparatus** to cool down **before** taking any mass or volume measurements. Also, state at what temperature the measurements were taken.

Fig 3.2

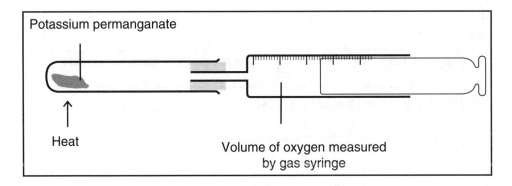

Potassium permanganate

Heat

Volume of oxygen measured by gas syringe

Results (all measurements were taken at 20 °C)

BEFORE HEATING:mass of test tube + Pot. mang.(VII)   = 2.19 g

AFTER HEATING: mass of test tube + residue   = 2.10 g

So,   **loss of mass** = 2.19 g – 2.10 g = 0.09 g

Looking at the word equation, it is clear that the loss in mass is, in fact, the **MASS OF OXYGEN** released.

> **Potassium Permanganate(VII) Heating Solid Residue + Oxygen**
> (2.19 g)   (2.10 g)   +   (0.09 g)

Total mass at start = 2.19 g   Total mass at end = 2.19 g

VOLUME OF OXYGEN collected in the gas syringe = 70 cm³

Thus, M = 0.09 g, V = 70 cm³,   D = ?

$$D = \frac{M}{V}$$

$$= \frac{0.09 \text{ g}}{70 \text{ cm}^3}$$

$$= 0.0013 \text{ g cm}^{-3} \text{ at } 20 \text{ °C}$$

So from this experiment, the density of oxygen is found to be 0.0013 g/cm³ at 20 ºC.

2) Finding The Density Of Carbon Dioxide

A similar experiment using the **same** apparatus can be carried out, this time by heating a suitable carbonate (e.g.copper carbonate) instead of potassium permanganate.

The experimental procedure is exactly the same, it is the **reaction** which is different.

e.g.

> **Copper Carbonate   HEATING   Copper Oxide + Carbon Dioxide**

3) Finding The Density Of Air

Fig 3.3 Finding the density of air

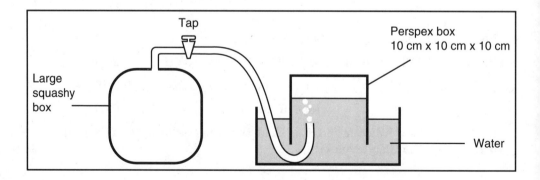

The diagram shows apparatus you may well have used to do this experiment.

1) Find the mass of the 'squashy box'.

2) Pump as much air (EXTRA AIR) as possible into the box and weigh again.

3) When the tap is opened, the 'extra air' comes out and displaces the water from the upturned perspex box.

4) Count the number of perspex boxes filled with 'extra air'- this gives the volume of the 'extra air'.

Readings:

Mass of container $= \mathbf{C}$ g

Mass of container + Extra Air $= (\mathbf{C} + \mathbf{E})$ g

So,　　Mass of Extra Air $= (\mathbf{C} + \mathbf{E})$ g $- \mathbf{C}$ g

$= \mathbf{E}$ g

Volume of perspex box, 10 cm $\times$ 10 cm $\times$ 10cm $= 1\,000$ cm^3

Number of boxes collected $= \mathbf{B}$

So,　　**volume of Extra Air** $= 1\,000 \times \mathbf{B}$ cm^3

To calculate the density of the Extra Air:

$M = \mathbf{E}$ g, $V = 1\,000\,\mathbf{B}$ cm^3,　　　$D = ?$

$$D = \frac{M}{V} = \frac{\mathbf{E}\ \text{g}}{1000 \times \mathbf{B}\ \text{cm}^3}$$

(A reasonable figure for the density of 'normal' air is 0.0012 g/cm^3)

Air	0.0012 g/cm^3
Carbon Dioxide	0.0016 g/cm^3
Hydrogen	0.00009 g/cm^3
Oxygen	0.0013 g/cm^3

Some Densities Of Gases At 20 °C

Density helps to discover unknown gases in the air.

When gases are cooled, they change into liquids.At one time, it was thought that the air was about 80% nitrogen, 20% oxygen and small quantities of carbon dioxide and water vapour (depending on the humidity). The following table shows what happens when air is cooled (usually at high pressure).

Temperature	Event	What Remains
20°C	Normal air	Nitrogen, Oxygen, Carbon Dioxide, Water Vapour
0°C	Water becomes solid	Nitrogen, Oxygen, Carbon Dioxide
-32°C	Carbon Dioxide becomes solid	Nitrogen, Oxygen,
-183°C	Oxygen becomes liquid	Nitrogen

When the remaining 'nitrogen' from the air was changed into a liquid, it was found that the density of the liquid was **greater** than the density of pure liquid nitrogen which had been produced as a result of a chemical reaction. This meant that the 'nitrogen' of the air remaining, when all the other gases had been removed, contained **more** than just nitrogen.

In fact the extra gases turned out to be the unreactive 'Noble' gases (argon being the most abundant) which are present in the air. It was the knowledge and application of the physical property, **density**, which helped lead the way to this discovery.

What Do You Know About Density?

1. What **two** things do you need to know about a substance in order to be able to find out its density?

2. Using the words *density*, *mass* and *volume*, write down the equation which you would use to find density.

3. Write down the **unit** of density.

4. The density of gold is 19.3 g/cm³.
    Write out the *density statement* in the form that you would use to:
    (i) Find the **MASS** of a known volume of gold.
    (ii) Find the **VOLUME** of a known mass of gold.

5. Find the **densities** of the following blocks of materials:
    (a) Material A, mass 750 g, volume 100 cm³.
    (b) Material B, mass 220 g, volume 20 cm³.
    (c) Material C, mass 540 g, volume 200 cm³.
    (d) Material D, mass 162 g, volume 60 cm³.

6. In question 5, which of the blocks A,B,C,D are made of the *same* material? Explain and give reasons for your answer.

7. The density of softwood is 0.6 g/cm³.
    What is the mass of:
    (a) 1 cm³,   (b) 5 cm³,   (c) 20 cm³,   of softwood?

8. The density of water is 1g/cm³.
    What is the mass of water in a box which measures 30 cm × 50 cm × 20 cm?

9. The density of perspex is 1.2 g/cm³. What is the volume of:
    (a) 1.2 g,   (b) 12 g,   (c) 108 g,   (d) 312 g of perspex?

10. The density of marble is 3.2 g/cm³; the density of glass is 2.8 g/cm³.
    (a) If you had 3 kg of each, which material would have the larger volume?
    (b) Which would have the greater mass; 6 cm³ of marble or 8 cm³ of glass?

11. Take the density of petrol as 0.8 g/cm³ and that the petrol tank of your car has a capacity of 50 litres (1 litre = 1 000 cm³). How much **extra** mass is added to the car when:
    (a) 10 litres of petrol are added.
    (b) The tank is completely full.

More Questions On Density

1. A cube of metal has a mass of 216 g and the density of the metal is 8 g/cm³. What is the length of each side of the cube?

2. Water has a density of 1 000 kg/m³. What is the mass of 240 cm³ of water (in kg)?

3. A block has dimensions 5 cm × 10 cm × 25 cm and its mass is 1.5 kg.
    Will it float in water? Support your answer with relevant calculations.

4. A 10 cm depth of snow falls onto a flat roof which is 20 m long and 20 m wide.
    The average density of snow is 0.12 g/cm³.
    (a) What is the volume of snow on the roof?
    (b) What is the mass of snow on the roof?
    (c) What volume of water will be formed when the snow melts?

5. A pile of wooden blocks, with each block measuring 15 cm × 20 cm × 1.5 cm, has a total volume of 27 000 cm³. The density of the wood is 0.6 g/cm³.
    All of the blocks are put into a container which has a volume of 30 000 cm³ and a mass (when empty), of 4.8 kg.
    (a) How many wooden blocks are there in the container?
    (b) What is the overall density of the container when all of the wooden blocks are in it?

6. An object has a mass of 75 kg. When the object is immersed in water, in a square tank of sides 0.5 m, the water rises by 0.1m.
    (a) What is the volume of the object (in cm^3)?
    (b) If the density of water is $1g/cm^3$, how much denser is the object than water?

7. A medal, 0.2 cm thick and diameter of 4 cm, is to be coated with a layer of gold which is 2×10^{-5} cm thick. Use the following assumptions to find an approximate cost of the gold used.
    (Density of gold is 20 g/cm^3; cost of gold is £6/g; $\pi = 3$)

8. 150kg of crude oil spills into the sea. An oil slick 1km wide and one molecule thick is formed.
    If the density of crude oil is 0.98 g/cm^3 and the diameter of a crude oil molecule is 10^{-7} cm, how long will the oil slick be?

9. If the density of air is $1.3 \times 10^{-3} g/cm^3$, what is the mass of air in a room measuring   10 m $\times$ 6 m $\times$ 3 m?

10. A central heating oil tank has sprung a leak and oil is flowing out at a rate of 4 g/s (s = second). There were originally 200 litres of oil in the tank. (density of oil is 0.8 g/cm^3, 1 litre is 1 000 cm^3)
    (a)What was the mass of oil in the tank at the start?
    (b)How long will the tank take to empty?

4   FORCES I: Make It Happen!

"It fell off the bench by itself, sir", is not an excuse which will be accepted by any physics teacher, because the teacher would know that the object which fell off the bench was given a push!

We say that a **force** was made **to act on** the object.

Quite simply,

> A force is a push or pull

Examples of pushes and pulls (forces):

1. Lifting is a pull upwards.
2. Pressing down is a push downwards, or against something.
3. Steering a bicycle is done by pulling on one side of the handlebars.
4. When stopping a bicycle, we pull the brake lever which causes the brake pads to push against the wheel.
5. Muscles, though, can only **pull**. When you bend your leg, muscles at the back of the leg contract and pull the leg. When you want to straighten the leg, it is the muscles at the front of the leg which contract to pull the leg straight.

What Can A Force Do?

It can:
    (a) make a stationary object move;
    (b) make a moving object go faster (accelerate), or slow down;
    (c) make a moving object change direction;
    (d) make a moving object stop;
    (e) change the shape of an object.

Some Other Facts About Forces

Forces are invisible

We cannot see a force. We can only see what a force does. It is rather like the wind - we cannot see it as such but we can see from the bending of branches on trees if there is a wind and if it is a strong or light wind. Something invisible exerts a pushing force on the branches causing them to bend.

Equilibrium: Forces acting in pairs in opposite directions

If a book is resting on a table then the book exerts a downward force on the table because it is being pulled towards the Earth's centre by gravity. The table exerts an upward force on the book as it resists the book's downwards force. Because these two forces are equal in size and act in opposite directions, there is no movement.

In this case,

> The forces are in equilibrium

If you find it hard to imagine a table exerting an upward force, think of a chair which is not strong enough to support your weight! In this case, the force exerted by you downwards, is greater than the force exerted by the chair upwards, and so movement results!

We have seen this when we looked at floating and sinking.

When an object floats, the upward force (upthrust) is equal to the downward force (weight) of the object.

When an object sinks, the downward force (weight) of the object is greater than the upward force (upthrust), so the object moves downwards, in the direction of the greater force, i.e. it sinks.

Size, direction

We have seen that when an object sinks, it is because the downward force is **greater** than the upward force and so the object moves downwards. This tells us that a force has size (sometimes called **magnitude**) and acts in a particular direction.

We measure the **size** of a force in **newton (N)**.

We show the **direction** of a force by an arrow . The arrowhead *points in the direction that movement, if it happens, will take place.*

Fig 4.1 Floating And Sinking

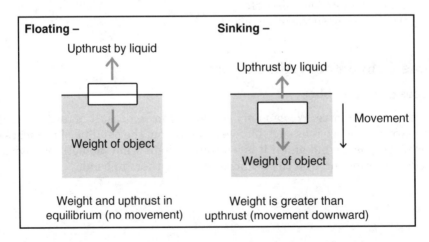

SCALAR and VECTOR quantities

Mass, length and density **only have size(magnitude)** - these are examples of **SCALAR** quantities.

Forces have **size magnitude AND direction** - these are examples of **VECTOR** quantities.

Adding Scalar Quantities

e.g. adding masses: 3 kg + 3 kg = 6 kg

This will **always** be true. The 6 kg is the result of adding the two masses 3 kg and 3 kg together .

Adding Vector Quantities

Because forces are Vector quantities, we have to take into account the **direction** of a force as well as its size.

Thus, for vector quantities, 3 N + 3 N does **not always** = 6 N.

i) Forces of 3 N and 3 N acting in the same direction, add up to give a **total** force (the **resultant force),** of 6 N.

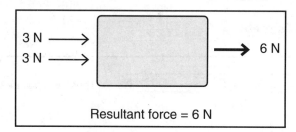

Resultant force = 6 N

ii) Forces of 3 N and 3 N can cancel each other out if they are acting in opposite directions.

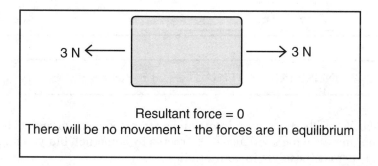

Resultant force = 0
There will be no movement – the forces are in equilibrium

Remember that a resultant force is a vector quantity, so when you describe it, you **must always** give **two** facts about it, namely (i) **its siz**e and (ii) **its direction**.

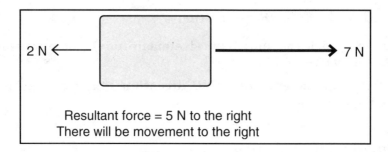

Resultant force = 5 N to the right
There will be movement to the right

Types Of Force

1. Magnetic Force

You will know that if you suspend a magnet so that it is able to rotate freely, it will come to rest in the same direction each time you repeat the experiment. It will **always** have the **same end** pointing towards the geographical North Pole so we call this particular end the **North seeking pole** and the other end the **South seeking pole**.

The needle of a compass is a small magnet.

How Magnets Behave

Fig 4.2. Magnets

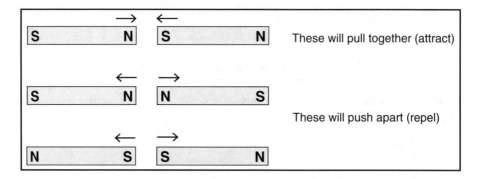

UNLIKE POLES ATTRACT — LIKE POLES REPEL

Note: ONLY objects containing **iron** will be attracted by a magnet. (There are a few other metals which will also be attracted by a magnet, but you might not have come across these yet in your studies.)

ONLY ANOTHER MAGNET will repel a magnet - this is the **best** way to identify a magnet.

Magnetic Field

This is the area around a magnet where magnetic force can be detected. The magnetic field can be shown using a plotting compass or iron filings. When using iron filings, these produce certain patterns in lines.

The lines are called LINES OF FORCE and show us the lines along which magnetic forces act. The arrows on the diagram below show the direction that a compass would point if it were placed on the lines.

The **spacing** between the lines of force tell us about the **strength** of the magnetic field. Where the lines are close together, the field is stronger than where the lines are further apart.

Remember that the **lines are invisible** and you only see them because iron filings will 'line up' along them when they are sprinkled over a magnet or magnets (preferably one which has been covered with a sheet of paper!).

Fig 4.3 Magnetic Fields

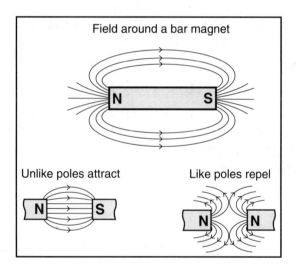

Why Do Some Pieces Of Iron Become Magnets?

This is really to do with the arrangement of the particles within the pieces of iron. Try to imagine that each particle acts as a tiny magnet. When all the particles are lined up, then the bar of iron will become a magnet.

The particles will tend to maintain their alignment, thus the magnetic iron is called a **permanent magnet.** It will remain a permanent magnet until the particles are jumbled up again.

This will happen if you:
    (i) heat a magnet;
    (ii) vibrate the particles, by knocking or hitting the magnet.

If either of these happens, then the magnet will lose its magnetism.

Fig. 4.4

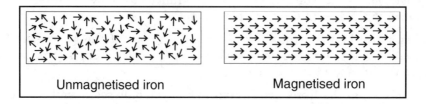

| Unmagnetised iron | Magnetised iron |

2. Electric Force

The modern word 'electricity' comes from the Ancient Greek word 'ELECTRA' which means **AMBER**. The Ancient Greeks found that when a rod of amber (a type of mineral) was rubbed with silk or fur, it attracted small objects. The rod was said to be **charged with electricity** and the force which caused small objects to move was called an **electrical force**.

Types Of Charge And How They Behave

You will remember experimenting with strips of acetate and polythene which have been charged by rubbing them with a duster. A summary of the results which you will have obtained is given below.

Fig. 4.5 (suspended rod)

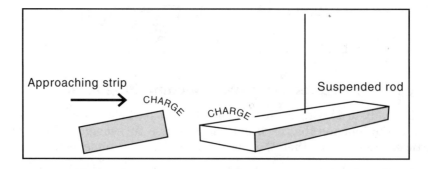

Results

Approaching strip	Suspended charged strip	
	Polythene	Acetate
Charged Polythene	attracts	repels
Charged Acetate	repels	attracts
Uncharged Polythene	attracts	attracts
Uncharged Acetate	attracts	attracts

This series of experiments tells us three important facts about electrical charges and forces. charge

> 1. There are two different types of charge — POSITIVE and NEGATIVE.
> 2. Like charges repel — unlike charges attract.
> 3. A charged body will attract any uncharged* body.

* We shall see later, that an uncharged body is really one in which there are equal numbers of positive and negative charges, thus the overall charge which the body has, is neither positive nor negative.

3. Gravitational Force

Two important features:

Any two objects will be attracted to each other by Gravitational Force (G/F).
The **size** of the force depends upon:

      (i) the masses of the objects;
      (ii) the distance between the centre of each mass.

> 1. It is the force of attraction between **any** masses.
> 2. Gravity **never pushes** – it only **pulls**.

Thanks to the work carried out by Sir Isaac Newton, we know that

$$G/F \text{ is proportional to } \frac{m_1 \times m_2}{d^2}$$

or,

$$G/F = G\left(\frac{m_1 \times m_2}{d^2}\right)$$

where G is a constant figure (in the same way as it is π), called the **GRAVITATIONAL CONSTANT**.

Fig. 4.6 Gravitational Force

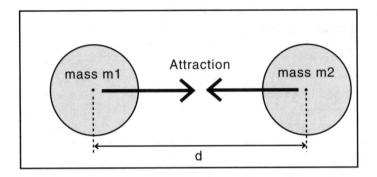

Note that the product of the masses is divided by the **square of the distance** between the centres. The whole relationship is known as the **inverse square law**. You will certainly meet this later on, for it is a fundamental law of physics and you will use it to determine the size of electrical, magnetic and gravitational forces.

You are not expected to remember the above equation and it is unlikely that you will use it at all at this stage, but it has been included to indicate a few things about G/F that you *should* be able to deduce, by studying it carefully.

(i) Clearly, if you **increase the masses** m_1, m_2, or both, then you will **increase** the magnitude of G/F.

(ii) If you **increase the distance** between the centres of the two masses, then you will **decrease** the size of G/F. (This means that gravitational force is **inversely** proportional to the **square of the distance** between the centres of masses - hence the name, *inverse square law!*)

(iii) Let us say that m_1 represents a planet and m_2 represents a body which is attracted towards the planet's centre.

Different values of m_1 will give different values of G/F depending upon which planet you are on. Thus those planets with larger masses will have bigger values for G/F than those with smaller masses.

(iv) In Outer Space, there will be no m_1. In this case $m_1 = 0$ and thus, looking at the equation, the value of G/F = 0.

Gravity In Action

1. G/F holds the Earth (and the other planets in our Solar System) in orbit around the Sun.

If you whirl an object on a string around your head and let go, then the object will fly off in a straight line. This is the principle of the athletics events of throwing the hammer and discus.

In figure 4.7, G/F is the 'invisible string' which prevents the Earth from flying out into Space and holds it in orbit round the Sun.

Fig 4.7

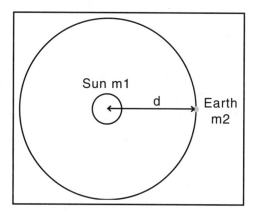

2. The Bails fall to the ground in both England and Australia.

Fig 4.8 **The bails (m_2) are attracted to the centre of the Earth (m_1) by G/F**

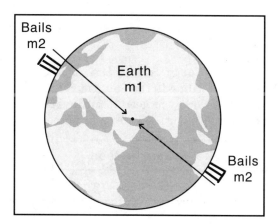

This is an important example as it explains why all objects fall to the ground when they are dropped and why all masses on Earth have **WEIGHT**.

Weight

3. All masses will be pulled towards the Earth's centre by G/F.

This means that on Earth, all masses will exert a downwards force.This force is called the object's **WEIGHT** and is measured in newton. The unit of G/F is N/kg.

On Earth, gravity exerts a force of approximately 10 N for every 1kg of mass. This means that a 1kg mass will have a WEIGHT of 10 N.

This can be confirmed by the use of a Spring Balance calibrated in newtons (sometimes called a Newtonmeter).
Look at the results of an experiment:

Mass	Weight (reading on spring balance)
1kg	10N
2kg	20N
5kg	50N
0.5kg	5N

From these results, it is straightforward to see that

$$\text{WEIGHT (N) = mass (kg)} \times \text{G/F (N/kg)}$$

Travels Of A 5kg Mass

Note:
(i)   **Mass remains constant** in value, *wherever* it is.
(ii)   **Weight changes** according to the value of G/F.
(iii) As the unit of G/F is N/kg, you need to **make sure that you work in kg for the mass** - convert, e.g. from grammes,

Earth	Earth's Moon	Outer Space
G/F =10N/kg	G/F =1.6N/kg	G/F =0
mass = 5kg	mass = 5kg	mass = 5kg
weight = 5kg x 10N/kg	weight = 5kg x 1.6N/kg	weight = 5kg x 0N/kg
= 50N	= 8N	= 0*

* This is why masses become weightless in Space.

4. FRICTIONAL Force

Let us begin by looking at an important law of physics - the **Law of Inertia**.

"A body at rest will remain at rest, unless the action of a force causes it to move......"

This is straightforward and easy to confirm, say, when we place a book on a table, we expect it to remain there!

".... a body in motion will continue to move at the same speed and in the same straight line direction, unless a force acts on it to change this."

This is **not** so easy to demonstrate on Earth, because there are **always** forces acting on moving bodies preventing them from moving forever in a straight line and at a constant speed.

For example, a bullet fired horizontally from a gun will eventually fall to Earth because:

(i) gravity acts on the mass of the bullet pulling it downwards all the time;

(ii) the moving bullet rubs against air particles which slow it down i.e. the air offers resistance to the motion.

The air is, in fact, exerting a **force which opposes the motion** of the bullet. This force is called **FRICTION**.

When **ANY** two surfaces rub together, there exists a force of friction between them which will try to oppose the movement.

What Causes Friction?

Think of a slide at a playground. The surface down which you slide is usually made of polished metal which is quite smooth. You will know that the slide would not be so much fun if its surface was covered in carpet!

Clearly, there is less friction between two smooth surfaces than there is between two rough surfaces.

So, in order to reduce friction between two surfaces, we have to make them as smooth as possible. However, even the smoothest of surfaces are not entirely flat when looked at through powerful electron microscopes. The various atoms and molecules form ridges and high spots.

Fig 4.9 A highly magnified view of two 'smooth' metal surfaces - showing 'high spots'.

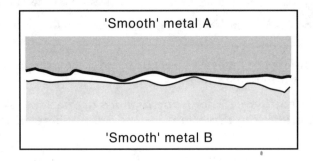

A powerful microscope will show that the two metals will have a bumpy ride as they move past one another. There is also a tendency for the high spots to stick together. Both of these factors contribute to the force (Friction) which tries to stop surfaces sliding past one another. A way of reducing friction is by keeping the surfaces slightly apart by coating them with a thin layer of oil. This is called **lubrication**. Sometimes air is used as a lubricant. A hovercraft rides on a cushion of air which reduces friction between it and the ground - this is why a ride on a hovercraft is called a flight!

Friction In Action

1. Road surfaces are rough and tyres have patterned ridges (tread) to **increase** friction between vehicles and the road, thus making the vehicles easier to control. Tyres which have smooth flat surfaces because the tread is worn down, are dangerous and illegal.

This is because a worn tyre, together with water, oil or ice on the road causes a great reduction in friction, making the vehicle less easy to control.

2. Polished, shiny floors and ice are difficult to walk across safely, because there is **less** friction between these surfaces and your shoes than you would be used to, when you are walking on normal rough surfaces.

3. Brake pads are designed to produce as **large** a frictional force as possible, in order to reduce the movement of the wheel, or to stop it altogether.

4. Ball bearings reduce the area of the moving axle in contact with the fixed bearing. This, together with the rolling action, reduces the force of friction between the two.

Fig 4.10 Bearings

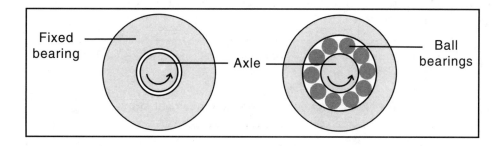

5. The tip of a snooker cue has chalk put on it to increase the friction between it and the ball so that you can hit the ball in a particular way, without the cue tip slipping.

Topspin, backspin and swerves would not be possible unless there was friction between the cue and the ball. Think also, what a game of snooker would be like if the cloth, which provides the necessary friction for the balls to slow down, was not there and the game was played on the smoother, slate surface which is underneath the cloth!

> Friction is a force which opposes motion.

Friction Also Prevents Movement From Starting

Consider trying to pull a heavy box across a carpeted floor. You give it a tug, but it does not move because of the friction between the box and the floor. Look at the diagram in fig 4.11.

As you pull harder, the force of friction increases, keeping the box still. You pull even harder and suddenly the box moves. This means that your pulling force is now greater than the upper limit of friction between the box and the floor.

Fig 4.11

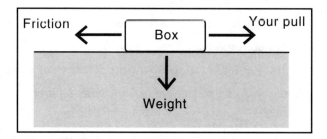

If you put the same box on a polished, wooden floor and pulled it, you would find that the same would happen as in the previous example, but in **this** case you would need **less** of a pull to pass the upper limit of friction between the box and the floor.

Thus, the force of friction between two stationary bodies
can vary from 0 to an upper limit.

The upper limit being when the movement **starts**.

Imagine that you are sitting on a highly-polished, wooden chair. If you sit carefully upright you will remain still. The smallest amount of movement could change the position of your body-weight causing a sideways force to act on the chair. This force may well be greater than the upper limit of friction between you and the polished chair causing you to slide off it! A way of making the chair easier to sit on, as well as making it more comfortable, would be to cover the seat with a material, such as fabric, which has a much higher upper limit of friction than polished wood.

What Do You Know About Forces And Movement?

1.   What is a force?

2.   What is the unit of force?

3.   What apparatus would you use to measure a force?

4.   Draw a diagram to show the forces acting on a floating body.

5.   List **five** things that a force can do.

6.   Explain what we mean when we talk about 'Forces in equilibrium'.

7.   Write **three** things which describe how magnets behave.

8.   Explain why one end of a magnet is called the 'North seeking Pole' and show how this fact can be arrived at.

9.   Describe **two** ways in which a permanent magnet can lose its magnetism.

10. What is meant by a magnetic field?

11. Draw the magnetic field around a bar magnet.

12. What are 'Lines of Force'?

13. Explain how lines of force tell us about the strength of a magnetic field.

14. What is the name given to the *type of movement* (forces) when electric charges and magnets:
     (i) push?   (ii) pull?

15. Show, with diagrams, electric charges (i) pushing (ii) pulling.

16. (a) What is Gravitational Force?
    (b) What is special, in terms of pulling and pushing, about Gravitational Force?

17. What is meant by the term Weight?

18. What are the units of : (a) Gravitational Force (b) Weight?

19. Explain the **difference** between Mass and Weight.

20. Which **two** things determine the size of Gravitational Force?

21. Draw labelled diagrams to show two different ways in which G/F acts.

22. Write down the equation used to calculate the weight of a body, include all units.

23. Given that G/F on Earth is 10 N/kg, calculate the **weight** of the following masses:
    i) 3 kg   ii) 30 kg   iii) 180 kg   iv) 500 g   v) 320 g

24. Given that G/F on Earth is 10N/kg, calculate the **Mass** of the following weights:
    i) 20 N   ii) 40 N   iii) 10 000 N   iv) 48 N   v) 1N

25. The Gravitational Force on the Earth is about 10N/kg and on the Moon is about 1.6 N/kg.
    An astronaut has a mass of 40 kg on Earth.
    i)   What is his mass on the Moon?
    ii) What is his weight on the Earth?
    iii) What is his weight on the Moon?

26. What is Friction?

27. What can friction **NEVER** do?

28. List **two** things that can be done to make friction between two surfaces as small as possible.

29. Think of a bicycle and list **four** parts of it where friction is evident. In **each case,** say if friction is a help or a nuisance.

30. What do we mean when we say that the force of friction between any two stationary bodies can change in value? Give an example to illustrate your answer.

FORCES II: Changing Shape (Elasticity)

If you take a ball of plasticine and push against opposite sides you will flatten it and you will have changed its shape permanently. If, however, you exert the same forces on a tennis ball, again the ball will flatten, but it will return to its original shape when you remove the pressing forces.

Bodies which are able to **change shape** when a force is exerted on them **and return** to their original shape when the force is removed, are said to be **elastic**.

> **Remember:** There is no such substance as Elastic.
> **Elastic** is a word to describe **how a substance behaves.**

Elastic Bodies And Bouncing

You will know that a tennis ball will bounce higher on concrete than it will on soft grass. Have you ever thought why this is so? Have a look at the table below.

	Elastic body (tennis ball)	Non-elastic body (plasticine)
Elastic surface (Foam rubber)	Poor bounce	Good bounce
Non-elastic surface (Concrete)	Good bounce	No bounce

You will see from the table that if **both** the falling body **and** the surface are elastic, the bounce will be very poor. So, to ensure good bounce, only **one** of the falling body and surface must be elastic.

We make use of this fact when we select materials for floors in laboratories and workshops. A glass bottle is much more likely to break on a hard-tiled floor than it is on an elastic cushion floor surface.

Of course, there are other considerations when choosing floor materials, such as colour, cost and water resistance, but elastic properties are also considered.

Think of a chair cushion filled with an elastic material - such as foam. This is soft and squashes to your shape when you sit on it. It returns to its original shape when you stand up.

Because it changes shape to accommodate the softness of your body, it is much more comfortable to sit on for long periods than a hard, unyielding, wooden chair.

Even so, wood can be shown to be elastic. Take, for example, a bow used for shooting arrows. The wood bends as the bow is pulled back and it returns to its original shape as the bowstring is released. Whilst the bow is pulled back, there is a **STRAIN** force in the wood. It is this strain force which enables the bow to return to its original shape when the arrow is shot.

All musical instruments make sounds because an elastic *something* (reed, string, drumskin, lip) changes shape many times a second producing vibrations. When the force is removed, the vibrating part of the instrument returns to its original shape. A tuning fork is a good example of this.

Springs As Elastic Bodies

You might be familiar with this experiment.

A spring is suspended from a laboratory clamp. Its length is measured. Masses are attached to the spring and the spring becomes longer. The new length of the spring is measured and the process is repeated. Results are presented as a table and often a graph is drawn to show what has happened.

When drawing the graph, remember that when you are measuring the various lengths of the spring, that it is these which are put on the 'y' axis of the graph.

> **When labelling graph axes: 'What is measured goes up the side'.**

Fig 5.1 Load-Extension graph of a spring

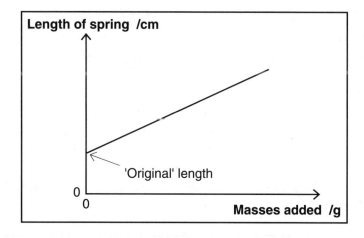

As we are really investigating the **change in length** when masses are added, we really only need to find the amount that the spring **EXTENDS** when each mass is applied.

To Calculate The Extension

| EXTENSION | = | NEW LENGTH minus ORIGINAL LENGTH |

Then we plot a graph of the EXTENSION caused by adding each mass.

Fig 5.2

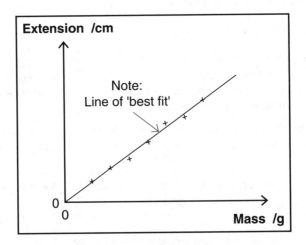

Note: Axes are labelled with quantity and unit — use either, "/cm" or, "in cm".

For the examples shown above, the spring will go back to its original length when the masses are removed, i.e. the spring is elastic. Also it will be noted from the straight line of the graph, that the extension is directly proportional to the load added.

If you repeat the experiment, but this time add more and more masses, there comes a time when the spring does not return to its original length - it has become deformed.

The load at which the spring becomes deformed is called the **LIMIT OF PROPORTIONALITY** (sometimes this can be called the Elastic Limit, but the two are not always the same). This is shown on the followinggraph. For loads greater than the elastic limit, the extension cannot be predicted, as it is not now proportional to the load applied.

Fig 5.3

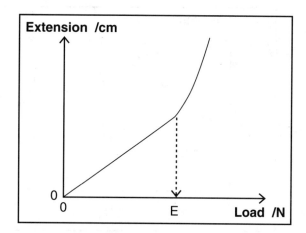

For loads 0 → E: The extension is proportional to the load applied, thus the extension can be predicted and the spring is elastic.

E is the LIMIT OF PROPORTIONALITY.

For loads greater than E: Because the Limit of proportionality has been exceeded, the extension is no longer proportional to the load, and cannot be predicted. The spring is permanently deformed, and when the loads are removed it will be longer than it was originally.

Springs are good examples of elastic bodies. Work on such elastic bodies was carried out by Robert Hooke and, after a great deal of experimentation, he was able to give us a Law which describes the elastic stretching of springs.

Hooke's Law:

When a force is applied to a spring, it will extend in direct proportion to the force applied and go back to its original length, provided that the elastic limit is not exceeded.

Fig 5.4

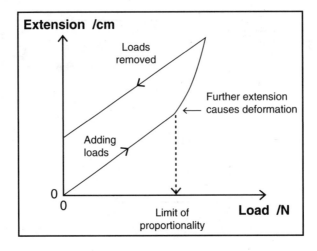

The graph above shows a spring that has been stretched past its elastic limit.

The Spring Balance (Sometimes called a Newtonmeter)

Because the extension of a steel spring is regular and directly related to the load applied, we can use such a spring as an instrument to measure force. There is always a mechanical 'stop' on such balances so that the spring's limit of proportionality is not exceeded.

As the spring stretches, the pointer shows how much extension is taking place.

For example:

    the spring stretches 1cm for a load of   1 N
    the spring stretches 2cm for a load of   2 N
    the spring stretches 3cm for a load of   3 N

The scale on the balance is a linear one with regular intervals, so it is a straightforward process when changing the readings on it from centimetre to newton. You will have used a spring balance to find the weight of various masses.

Most laboratories have a collection of different spring balances in order to be able to measure a wide range of forces.

For example:

A balance to measure forces from 0 N to 15 N -which uses a 'weak' spring.
A balance to measure forces from 0 N to 25 N - which uses a 'stronger' spring.
A balance to measure forces from 0 N to 100 N - which uses an 'even stronger' spring.

A rubber band would not be any use in such a measuring device, because its extension is **not at all regular** as loads are applied and so readings would be unreliable.

Combining springs (in this section, ALL the springs are similar)

1. Springs in Series (one after another)
For Springs in Series:

> Total Extension Of One Spring x Number Of Springs

Fig 5.5 Springs in Series (Assume that all springs in this example are similar)

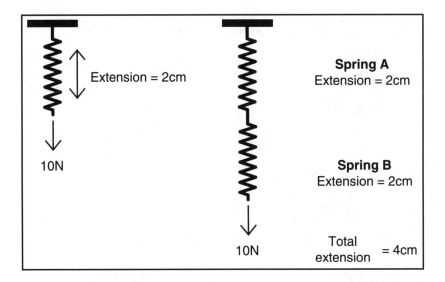

2. Springs in Parallel ("Sharing the load - Side by Side")

> Total Extension = Extension Of One Spring ÷ Number Of Springs

Fig 5.6 Springs in parallel (Assume that all springs in this example are similar)

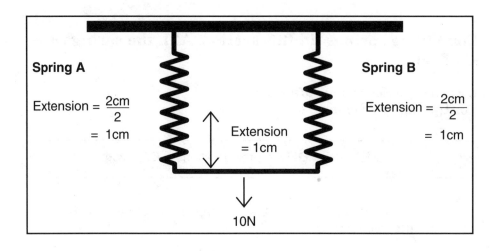

Extension And Compression Of Elastic Bodies

The suspension on some radio-controlled model cars contains springs which are compressed. As the car goes over a bump, the wheels are pushed upwards and the weight of the car pushes downwards. The suspension spring becomes squashed (**COMPRESSED**).

When the bump has been passed, the spring goes back to its original shape and the wheels are pushed down. Thus, the body of the car remains level whilst the wheels go up and down. Exactly like the function of **'Shock Absorbers'** in your family car.

You may have noticed that the saddle on your bicycle is supported by strong springs. These act as shock absorbers to make your ride as smooth as possible and work in the same way as the suspension springs on the model car described above.

If you look inside the mattress on your bed, you would find, if it was of the 'Interior Sprung' variety, that there would be a network of springs all in parallel with each other. As the load is shared between each of the springs, the mattress is able to support quite heavy weights. The springs compress when we lie on the bed and return to their original shape when we get off.

Other Ways Of Changing The Shape Of Elastic Materials

1. Bending

If you fix one end of a hacksaw blade in a vice and pull the other end sideways, the blade will bend. When you let go, the blade will return to its original position. You could support it so that it bent up and down, add masses, measure how far it bends and plot your results on a graph just as you did with springs.

However, if you apply too much force, you could well exceed the limit of proportionality and the blade will remain permanently bent. I expect that you have found out that plastic rulers behave in the same way and we have already mentioned the elastic properties of wood when we looked at how a bow shoots an arrow.

Construction engineers need to know about the elastic properties of the materials which they use and they will **expect** certain substances to extend and/or bend when loads are applied. In this case, they will be measuring the *size of load* which causes the material to change shape.

In these cases, the graph is plotted differently from the one which you would have plotted when you were trying to find out **how much extension** is produced for various loads.

Remember: 'What is measured, goes up the side'. So in this case, it is the **load** which is measured, resulting in the graph (Fig 5.7).

The metal used for car bodies has elastic properties - to a point! If you press gently on the body of a car, it will go in and spring out again when the force is removed. If a greater force is applied, permanent damage will result.

Sometimes, for small dents, the metal can be hammered gently back into shape.

Sadly, for larger dents, the metal has stretched beyond its limit of proportionality and permanent deformation has taken place. In this case, the only solution is to replace the entire door, bonnet or whatever, which is a costly exercise.

Fig 5.7 Extension-Load graph showing the Elastic Limit

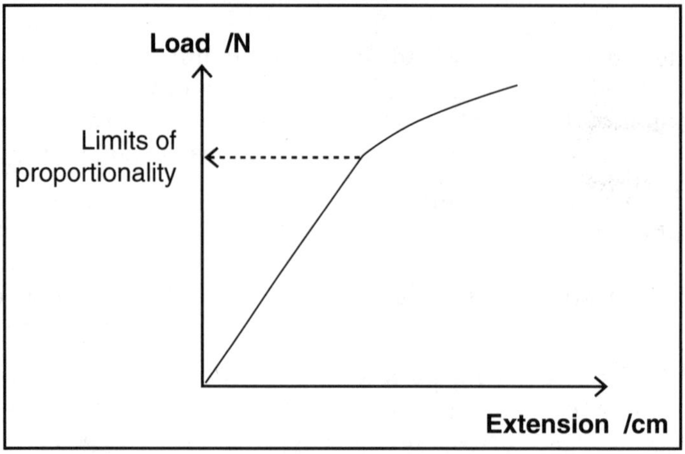

Coiling - A Special Form Of Bending

A clockwork spring is really a straight strip of metal (usually tempered steel) which has been coiled up on itself. Because of the elastic properties of the steel, it tries to uncoil and straighten itself. So, when you wind the strip into tight coils and let go, the coil unwinds as the strip tries to return to its original shape. In a clockwork motor, one end of the spring is fixed and the centre of the coil - which is attached to a driving axle - turns as the strip unwinds.

Twisting

Rubber-powered toys work because of the elastic properties of rubber (this is why we sometimes call rubber bands 'elastic bands').

If one end is fixed and the other end twisted then, when the force is removed, the rubber band will straighten and return to its original shape.

More twists mean that a greater force has been applied and this is why it becomes harder to twist the band for those final few turns.

Tension

When a body is extended, compressed, bent, coiled or twisted, the material is strained and experiences a force of **Tension** - just as you would, if you were bent or twisted! It is this force of tension which allows elastic bodies to return to their original shape.

> **Non-elastic materials** - such as plasticine - do not experience the same tension force and so do not go back to their original shape when the force is removed.

What Do You Know About Changing Shape (Elasticity)

1. What two things must a body be able to do to be described as an elastic body?

2. Name three things:
    (i) that are elastic;
    (ii) that are non-elastic.

3. What does the word extension mean when used in connection with experiments using springs?

Load / N	0	1	2	3	4	5	6	7	8	9
Length / cm	6	7	8	9	10	11	14	18	24	32
Extension										

4. (i) Copy out and complete the table below to show the extension for each load.
    (ii) Draw a graph to show how the extension changes as the load is increased.
    (iii) Will the spring return to its original load when the load is removed? Give a reason for your answer.

5. A spring is 6 cm long. When a load of 100g is attached to it, the new length is 8 cm. It returns to 6cm when the load is removed.
    (i) What will be the length when a load of 50 g is attached?
    (ii) What will be the length when a load of 75 g is attached?
    (iii)What will be the length when a load of 5 kg is attached?

6. An experiment was carried out to find out how a steel spring stretched when various forces are applied. The results are given below.

Force applied / N	1.0	1.5	2.0	3.0	4.0	5.0
Length of spring / mm	61.3	62.0	62.7	64.0	65.3	66.7

    Draw a graph to find out what the length was for a force of 4.5 N.

7. A spring extends 8 cm for a load of 100 g. What will be the total extension when a second similar spring is put in series with it and a load of 100 g is attached?

8. Using the two springs connected in series from question 7, what would be the extension for the following loads:
    (i) 200 g?   (ii) 50 g?

9. If the two springs from questions 7 & 8 are now connected in parallel, write down the extension for the following loads:
   (i) 100 g   (ii) 200 g   (iii) 50 g

10. Now FOUR springs, similar to the springs in questions 7, 8 & 9, are connected in parallel. Write down what the extension would be for the following loads:
    (i) 100 g   (ii) 200 g   (iii) 50 g

11. Look at the following arrangements of springs. In each case, all of the springs are similar.

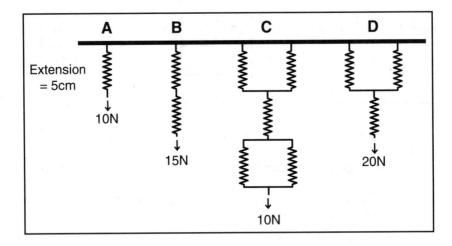

Write down what the total extension would be for the arrangements B, C, D & E.

12. The gravitational force on the moon is one sixth of its value on Earth. A spring stretches 18 cm when a force of 6 N is applied to it on Earth.
    (i) How much would it stretch on the moon when a force of 6 N is applied to it?
    (ii) What force would need to be applied on the moon to make the spring stretch 18 cm?

Further Questions On Elasticity

1. (i) Which Law describes the stretching of springs?
   (ii) Describe what this Law says and means as clearly and simply as possible. (Hint: you may need to use numbers in your answer.)

2. A single spring provides the following information:
   Total length when a force of 2 N is applied, is 14 cm
   Total length when a force of 7 N is applied, is 29 cm
   The elastic limit is passed at 10 N
   Two such (identical) springs are connected in parallel and the combination is pulled with a force of 8 N. What will be the length of each spring?

3. A spring is 19cm long with a load of 4 N and 27cm long with a load of 20 N.
    (a) What would be: (i) its length for a load of 2 N, (ii) the load on it for a length of 24 cm?
    (b) What was the original length of the spring?

4. A thin metal wire was hung from a beam and the length measured as weights were added to the bottom end of the wire.
    The following readings were taken:

Load / N	0	1	3	4	6	8	9	10
Length / mm	100	102	106	108	112	116	124	138

    (i) Plot these results on a graph in such a way that the LOAD is measured against the extension.
    (ii) What would you expect to happen when the 10 N load is removed?

5. Each spring in the diagram below stretches by 12 cm when a load of 10N is applied.
    The four springs are set up and a load of 5 N is hung at point Y.
    (i) How far does point X move when the load is applied?
    (ii) How far does point Y move when the force is applied?

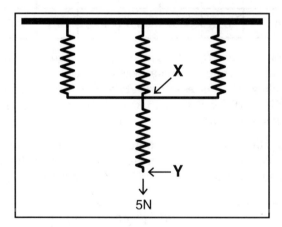

6. Masses are hung at the bottom end of a vertical spring which has an unstretched length of 100 mm.
    The following results are obtained:

Mass / g	0	100	200	300	400	500	600	700
Length / mm	100	142	161	226	268	310	385	531

(a) Using graph paper, plot a graph to show how the extension varies with the load applied.

(b) Why is it better to plot extension, rather than length?

(c) What would you expect the extension to be for a load of:

(i) 250 g?   (ii) 800 g?

7. The markings on a spring balance show intervals of 1N and are spaced 4 mm apart.

(a) What law does the spring inside the balance obey?

(b) How far will the spring extend when a force of 5 N is applied to it?

(c) By how much will the extension of the spring increase when the force applied to it changes from 5 N to 7 N?

8. An experiment was performed to measure the extension of a spring. The following results were obtained as the spring was being loaded:

Force / N	0	2	4	6	8	9	10	11
Extension / cm	0	1.1	2.1	3.4	4.6	6.0	7.5	12.0

On unloading the spring, the following results were obtained:

Force / N	11	10	9	8	6	4	2	0
Extension / cm	12.0	11.4	10.8	10.2	9.1	8.0	6.8	5.8

Plot a graph of these results and answer the following questions:

(i)   On loading, what extension was produced by a force of 7.5N?

(ii)   On loading, what force is needed to produce an extension of 4cm?

(iii) Describe, as fully as you can, what is happening to the spring during the loading and unloading.

9. A spring is clamped at its top and various masses are attached to the lower end. The length of the spring is measured each time the mass is altered. The results are shown in the order in which they were obtained.

Mass / g	0	20	40	60	40	20	0
Length / mm	101	103	105	107	105	103	101

Mass / g	40	60	80	100	80	60	40
Length / mm	105	107	110	114	112	110	108

(a) Plot a graph of extension of the spring (in mm) against the mass (in g) for the first seven readings. Draw a line through the points.

(b) Find from this graph the length of the spring if a mass of 50g had been attached.

(c) Continue the graph for the remaining seven points and draw a smooth dotted line joining up these points.

(d) The extensions in the last reading and the fifth reading are not the same, even though the masses are the same. Explain this carefully.

(e) If the masses are removed after the last reading, what would be the length of the spring?

10. A spring is used as a spring balance. It extends by 10.0 mm for each newton added, up to a maximum of 12 N.

Explain whether you would obtain greater accuracy in measuring a force of about 9 N by using four such springs in series rather than by using one on its own.

11. In an experiment, weights are hung from one end of a steel spring. The table shows successive readings of the weight on the end of the spring, and its total length, in the order in which they were taken.

Force (F) / N	4	6	8	10	8	6	4	2
Total Length (l) / cm	9.0	10.5	12.5	15.0	13.5	12.0	10.5	9.0

(i) While springs are extending in proportion to an applied force, they have a characteristic spring constant, k, defined by the equation

$$k = F/x$$

F is the force applied, and x is the total extension for that applied force. Calculate a value of k for the spring in the experiment, with an appropriate unit.

(ii) Comment on any other features of the data which you notice.

12. (i) Sandra and Joy have made a model bridge using balsa wood and want to see how strong it is. They test it by standing weights in the centre and measure how much the bridge has bent .

Their results are shown below:

Plot a graph of the bend (in mm), against the weight (in cm).

Weight / N	0	5	10	15	20	25	30
Amount of bend / mm	0	2	12	22	32	37	40

(ii) In a discussion on bridges, Sandra says that not only does the bridge have to be strong, but the supports on which it rests have to be strong too. Explain what you think she means.

(iii) Suspension bridges have the roadway hung from cables and the cables supported by towers. In what order, giving reasons, do you think that suspension bridges are built?

FORCES III: Turning It Around

Remove the handlebars from your bicycle. Now you are left with a round spindle pointing upwards. Try to turn the front wheel using this spindle and you will find it much more difficult than when the handlebars were there.

The handlebars make the task of turning the wheel **much easier** and are an example of a simple **machine**. Together, the handlebars form a **LEVER** which is able to turn about a fixed pivot (called a **Fulcrum**).

Handlebars would not be much use if they were made of a soft material, such as plasticine, so a lever is a rigid body.

> A **lever** is any rigid body which is able to turn about
> a **pivot** (fulcrum)
>
> Forces which cause levers to turn are called **turning moments.**

Size Of A Turning Moment

The size of a turning moment depends upon:
> (i) the size of the force;
> (ii) the perpendicular distance from the force to the fulcrum.

To calculate the size of a Turning Moment, we use the expression:

> Turning Moment   =   Force applied x distance
> (from the force to the fulcrum)

In Fig 6.1,

a	Turning Moment (50 Ncm)	= 10N × 5 cm
b	Turning Moment (40 Ncm)	= 10N × 4 cm
c	Turning Moment (30 Ncm)	= 10N × 3 cm
d	Turning Moment (20 Ncm)	= 10N × 2 cm
e	Turning Moment (10 Ncm)	= 10N × 1cm
f	Turning Moment (0)	= 10N × 0

Fig 6.1 Turning Moment Force Distance (force-fulcrum)

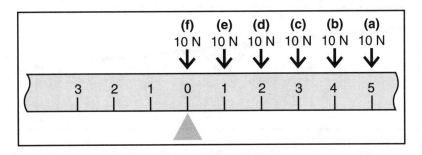

In (f) the TM = 0 so there is **no turning effect.**

Thus forces applied **at** the fulcrum do **not turn** a lever - they may well cause a strain on the fulcrum, but this is a different matter!

Forces Acting On A Lever

Consider a see-saw made from a plank of wood which is 2 m long and weighs 250 N. The plank is even and balances if it is supported in the middle. Thus, when the plank balances, the weight of it acts through the fulcrum. Clearly, you will need a fulcrum that is strong enough to push upwards with a force of at least 250 N or your see-saw will collapse.

All this information is summarised in the diagram below.

Fig 6.2 A plank in equilibrium at the fulcrum

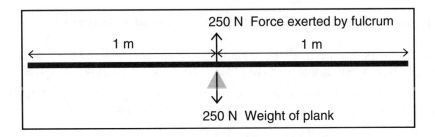

Now a friend, weighing 300 N, sits on the right hand end.
He will exert a Turning Moment of 300 N × 100 cm = 30 000 Ncm, so the lever turns.(See fig 6.3).

Fig 6.3 Turning Moment applied to one end of a plank

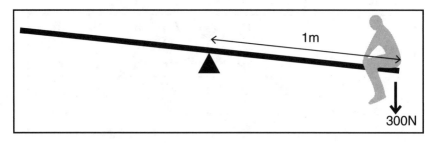

You are larger than your friend and have a weight of 500 N. If you sit at the left hand end, the Turning Moment on your side will be

500 N × 100 cm = 50 000 Ncm.

As this is bigger than the Turning Moment exerted by your friend, you will go down and he will go up.

Fig 6.4 Unequal turning moments at the two ends of a plank

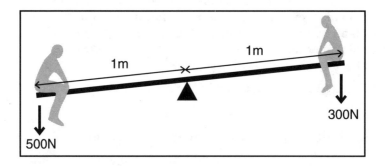

Where would you sit to make the see-saw balance?

Your friend exerts a TM of 30 000 Ncm and he causes the lever to turn (rotate) in a **CLOCKWISE** direction, so his TM is called the **CLOCKWISE MOMENT.**

When you sit on the see-saw you turn (rotate) it in an **ANTICLOCKWISE** direction - so your TM is called the **ANTICLOCKWISE MOMENT.**

Clearly, for the see-saw to balance
Let 'x' be the distance you must sit from the fulcrum.

The **anticlockwise moment** must equal the
clockwise moment

Thus when the see-saw balances: 500 N × *x* = 300 N × 100 cm
Dividing both sides by 500 N, gives

$$\frac{500N \times x}{500N} = \frac{300N \times 100cm}{500N}$$

Simplifying, we obtain $x = \dfrac{3 \times 100cm}{5}$

so   *x* = 60 cm

Thus, for the see-saw to balance, you must sit 60 cm from the fulcrum, while your friend sits right at the other end, i.e. 100 cm from the fulcrum. This result is summarised below:

Fig 6.5

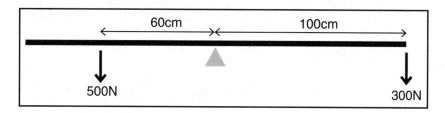

ANTICLOCKWISE MOMENT   CLOCKWISE MOMENT
      500 N × 60 cm   300 N × 100 cm
      TM: 30 000 Ncm   TM: 30 000 Ncm

Look at the diagram and the figures carefully and note:
   i) **that a smaller force is able to balance a larger force;**
  ii) **that the smaller force is further from the fulcrum than the larger force.**

Adding Extra Turning Moments

Your brother, who weighs 400 N, also wants to sit on the see-saw whilst you two are sitting at each end. If you move to the very end, where will your brother sit to make the see-saw balance?

Fig 6.6

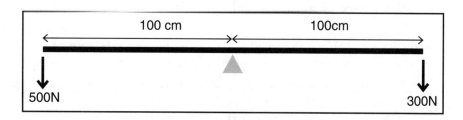

Clearly, your brother must sit on the Right Hand Side. Thus,

Fig 6.7

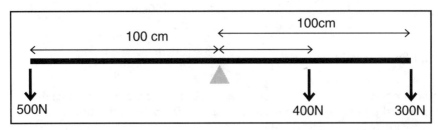

So:

> Anticlockwise Moments = (500N x 100cm)
> Clockwise Moments = (400N x xcm) + (300N x 100cm)

At balance, $(500\ N \times 100\ cm) = (400\ N \times X\ cm) + (300\ N \times 100\ cm)$

So $(500\ N \times 100\ cm) - (300\ N \times 100\ cm) = 400\ N \times x$

So $100\ cm\ (500\ N - 300\ N) = 400\ N \times x$

So $100\ cm \times 200\ N = 400\ N \times x$

So $\dfrac{100cm \times 200N}{400N} = x$

So $x = 50\ cm$

These two examples have been worked out in full for you, *to show you how to lay out* the solutions to these problems, thus demonstrating the **Law of Moments**, describing how levers behave.

Law Of Moments (Sometimes called the Lever Law)

> When a lever balances, the *sum* of the anticlockwise moments equals the *sum* of the clockwise moments.

Balance and Centre of Mass

Consider a well made metre ruler. If you support it with your finger at the 50cm mark it should not turn, but remain absolutely steady. We then say that it is balanced.

There is a downward force, the weight of the ruler, but this is being counteracted by the upward force which your supporting finger is exerting.

The weight of the ruler is acting at the 50cm mark. If you were to move your finger to the 40cm mark, the ruler would tip. This is because the downward force (weight) of the ruler is **still acting at the 50cm mark.**

Fig 6.8 Centre of gravity

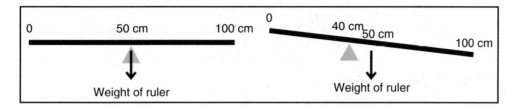

Clearly, the 50cm mark is a *"special place"* on the ruler - we call it the **CENTRE OF MASS** (sometimes it is called the **Centre of Gravity**).

Examples Of Levers In Action

Bicycle Handlebars

Fig 6.9 Bicycle handlebars

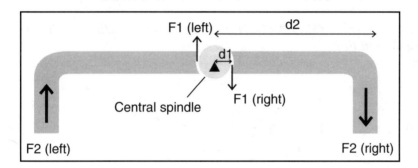

Look at the **Right Hand Side only**. There are **two** expressions for the force required to turn the handlebars to the right.

These are:

$F_1 \times d_1$ i.e. the turning force produced by exerting a force on the spindle.

$F_1 \times d_2$ i.e. the turning force produced by exerting a force at the end of the handlebar.

As **both** these Turning Moments do the **same job** then

$$F_1 \times d_1 = F_2 \times d_2$$

As d_1 is much **smaller** than d_2, then F_1 is much **larger** than F_2. (Put your own Figures in to test this.)

In this case, we are using a small force to move a large force. Thus a lever is a **simple machine.**

> So a **small force** which is a **large distance** from the fulcrum, balances a **larger force** which is a **short distance** from the fulcrum

What Is A Machine?

It is, quite simply, something which makes a task easier because it enables a small force to move a bigger one.

Fig 6.10 A spanner as a machine

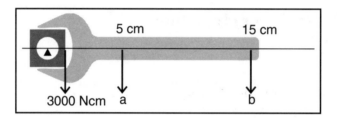

Say a nut needs a TM of 3 000 Ncm to make it turn. What are the values of forces (a) and (b)?

Force (a): $\quad a \times 5$ cm $= 3\,000$ Ncm

So $\qquad\qquad a = \dfrac{300\text{Ncm}}{5}$

$\qquad\qquad\quad = 600$ N

Force (b): $\quad b \times 15$ cm $= 3\,000$ Ncm

So $\qquad\qquad b = \dfrac{3000\text{Ncm}}{15}$

$\qquad\qquad\quad = 200$ N

So you can see that by applying the force at the **end** of the spanner, you will need a **smaller force** to turn the nut, than would be required if you had applied the force closer to the nut.

Now you should be able to work out why:-

i) a long-handled spade is much easier to dig soil, than a short-handled trowel;

ii) you should hold a hammer at the end of the handle to obtain the maximum force when hammering nails;

iii) door handles are placed as far away from the hinge (fulcrum) as possible;

iv) long door handles are easier to turn than door knobs.

Combining Levers

Scissors, pliers, secateurs and wire-cutters are all two levers which turn about the same pivot (fulcrum). The force you exert is called the **EFFORT** and the force exerted (i.e. the force which does the cutting) is called the **LOAD**.

Fig 6.11

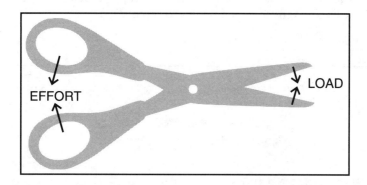

From the discussions above, you should see that cutting tools which are required to cut heavier loads have longer handles.

For example:

(a) Garden shears for cutting hedges have longer handles and blades than scissors used for cutting paper;

(b) Loppers for cutting small branches off trees have longer handles than secateurs used for cutting thin branches off small shrubs;

(c) Tin Snips used to cut metal sheet have longer handles than electrical wire cutters.

Pulleys

Diagram (a): One string is pulling upwards, so a force of 100 N is required.

Diagram (b): One string is pulling upwards, so a force of 100 N is still required, but the pulley enables the 100 N to be downward force - which may be easier.

Diagram (c): The downward force of 100 N is now shared by two strings, so the upward force in each string is 50 N. The top pulley causes the upward force of 50 N to be changed to a downward force of 50 N.

Fig 6.12

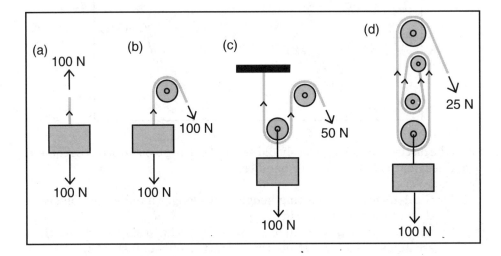

Diagram (d): The downward force of 100 N is now shared between four strings, so each string will exert an upward force of 25 N. This means that a force of 25 N can be used to lift a 100 N weight.

Thus,

> 1. A pulley changes the **direction** of a force.
> 2. A **set of pulleys** is a machine which enables a small force to move a larger force.

What About The Distances Travelled By Effort And Load Forces?

Look at the pulley system in diagram (c). If you pull with a force of 50 N for a distance of 20 cm, then the load will move $\dfrac{20cm}{2}$, which is 10 cm.

In diagram (d), if you pull with a force of 25 N for a distance of 20 cm then the load will move $\dfrac{20cm}{4}$, which is 5 cm.

So, to find out how far you have to pull a pulley string to lift a load by a certain amount:

Distance of Effort pull = distance the Load moves × number of pulley strings supporting the load.

We now see that, as well as reducing the force needed to move a load, a machine will change the distances moved by the Effort and Load forces. As a rule:

> If a machine magnifies the Effort force — the distance which the force moves will be smaller.

What Do You Know About Turning Forces?

1. Write down **two** features of a lever.

2. (a) What is a turning moment?
    (b) How can you calculate the size of a turning moment?

3. A man turns a nut by exerting a force of 300 Ncm at the end of a spanner which is 15 cm long. What is the turning moment applied to the nut?

4. If a turning moment of 8 Nm is produced at a point 0.8 m from the hinge of a door, what force was used to achieve this?

For questions **5, 6 ,7 & 8,**
   (i)   draw the levers, putting in all forces and distances;
   (ii) say if the lever is balanced or not;
   (iii) if the lever is unbalanced, say which way the lever turns.

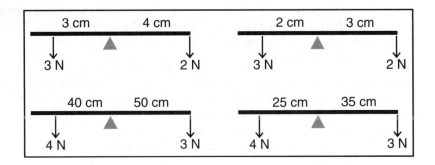

For questions **9, 10, 11, 12, 13 & 14**, find X in each case. Make sure that you use the correct units.

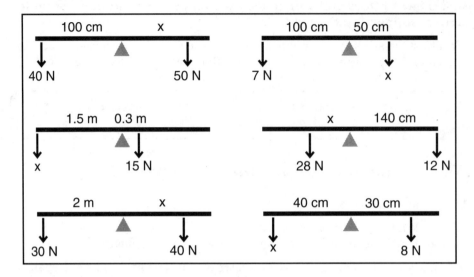

15. A boy of mass 40 kg sits 270 cm from the centre of a see-saw. A girl of mass 30 kg sits on the other side. Where must she sit to enable the lever to balance?

Further Questions on Turning Forces

1. Explain why, on most doors, the handle is placed far from the hinge.

2. A metre rule is suspended at the 50 cm mark. Weights are hung from it as follows: 2 N from the 10 cm mark; 3 N from the 30 cm mark; 8 N from the 40 cm mark and 6 N from the 60 cm mark. Where must a 4 N weight be hung to balance the rule?

3. The diagram below shows how an office hole-puncher works. The handle is depressed at A and the Punch acts at B. It takes a force at B of 0.25 N to punch a hole in one sheet of paper.

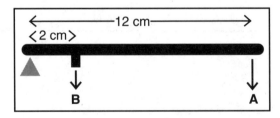

(i) Assuming that the force required to punch holes is proportional to the number of sheets of paper, what force will be required at B to punch six sheets of paper?

(ii) What force must be applied at A to punch six sheets of paper?

4. A bird nesting box is hung as shown in the diagram.

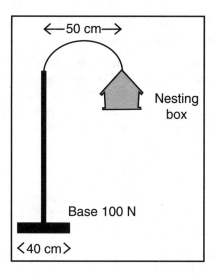

The nesting box and contents has a weight of 50 N and the system is stable. The box will fall over if its weight and contents is 75 N.

Ignoring the weight of the light rods which support the box, calculate the maximum weight of the box and contents which the construction will just support without toppling.

5. A metre rule is balanced as shown below.

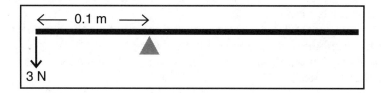

(i) Calculate the weight of the rule.
(ii) Calculate the upward force exerted by the fulcrum.

6.

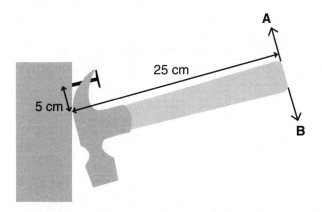

(i) Which force, A or B, should be used to pull out the nail? Explain your answer.

(ii) If a force of 250 N applied to the end of the hammer pulls out the nail, what force does the nail exert?

7. A metre rule weighing 1N, is suspended at the 40 cm mark. The rule balances when a weight of 5 N is suspended at the 10 cm mark and an unknown weight (X) is suspended at the 90 cm mark.

(i)   Draw a diagram of the above, putting in all forces and distances.

(ii) Calculate the value of the unknown weight X.

(iii) What is the total downward force?

(iv) What is the tension in the string?

8. Explain how, with the help of a suitable lever, you could use a spring balance (which can only measure forces up to 10 N), to measure the weight of a metal block which has a weight of 30 N. Draw a diagram of your result and include all forces and distances.

9. The diagram below shows a bar marked at equal intervals. The masses are all 10 g slotted masses.

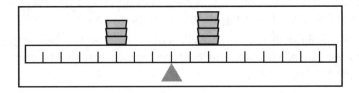

(i)   Why does the mass of the bar not matter in calculations in this particular example?

(ii) Jane says, 'There is more mass on the right, so the bar will tip to the right'. Explain carefully why Jane is wrong.

(iii) At which point would you put an extra 10 g slotted mass, to make the bar balance?

10. There is a uniform plank which is 1.00 m long and weighing 10 N. The plank is pivoted on a hinge at the left and the weight of the plank acts at the centre (50 cm mark). A block of metal is placed so that its weight acts 950 mm from the hinge. The plank is balanced by pulling the string upwards with a force of 120 N. The string is attached to the plank 250 mm from the hinge.

(i)   Draw a diagram of the arrangement.

(ii) What is the weight of the block of metal?

(iii) Assuming that the force of gravity is 10 N/kg, what is the mass of the block?

11. A trailer, in which there is a bag of cement weighing 500 N and a pile of bricks weighing 300 N, is being towed by a car. The cement is placed 60 cm behind the axle of the trailer, while the bricks are stacked so that their weight acts 120 cm in front of it. What is the vertical force on the towing bar of the car, if it is situated 200 cm in front of the axle of the trailer?

12. The diagram shows part of a weighing machine.

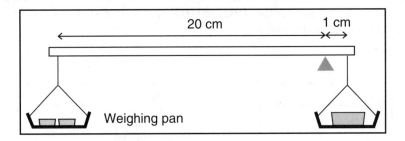

Identical metal blocks are placed in the left-hand pan to balance an unknown mass in the right-hand pan. For every 1 kg mass added to the right-hand pan, it is necessary to add one metal block to the   left hand pan.

(i)   What is the mass of one of the metal blocks?

(ii) If a 600g mass is added to the right-hand pan, balance may be restored by placing another metal block somewhere on the right-hand arm of the balance. How far from the pivot must this block be placed?

(iii) When an extra mass is added to the right-hand pan, the metal block [from (ii)] must be moved 4cm to the left. What is the value of this extra mass?

7 FORCES IV : Exerting Pressure

You will all know that cricket stumps are pointed at one end to make them easier to push into the (sometimes hard) ground. But have you ever considered the physics principle which is used in the design?

Clearly, the points are designed to increase the 'Sinkability' of the stump and this is done by increasing the **PRESSURE** which the stump exerts on the ground as it is being pushed in.

Fig.7.1

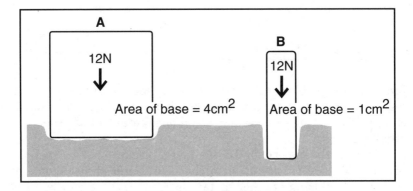

> The force acting on **each** cm² is known as **pressure**.

B will sink **further** than **A,** because it exerts **more pressure** on the ground than **A.**

Thus, to calculate the pressure exerted by one surface on another, we use the expression:

$$\text{PRESSURE} = \frac{\text{FORCE APPLIED}}{\text{AREA}}$$

So, **the Unit of Pressure is N/m²**

1 N/m² is also called 1 pascal (Pa), because it is named after Blaise Pascal, the scientist famous for his investigations of atmospheric pressure.

In fact, you are more likely to have measured area in cm² and so it is perfectly in order to measure pressure in N/cm².

PRESSURE IN ACTION

> Decreasing the area over which a force acts increases the Pressure.

Fig. 7.2
(i) Sports shoes - studs/spikes

Fig 7.3
(ii) Any sharp point/blade

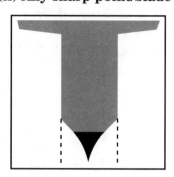

> Increasing the area over which a force acts decreases the Pressure.

Fig. 7.4 Tank/Caterpillar tracks

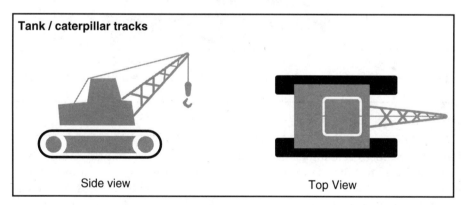

Tank / caterpillar tracks

Side view   Top View

Fig. 7.5 (ii) Skis, snow-shoes

PRESSURE IN LIQUIDS

> Pressure increases as you go deeper.

You will know that as you dive to the bottom of a swimming pool, you will feel your ears 'popping'. This is due to the pressure on your ear drum increasing because of the greater water pressure as you go deeper. You will be familiar with the demonstration below.

Fig. 7.6

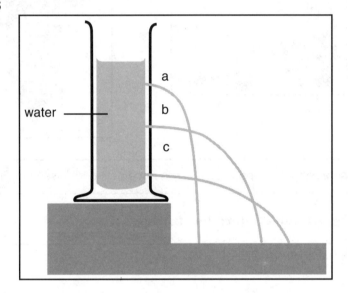

Jet *c* shoots out the furthest because the **pressure** of the liquid at *c* is **greater**.

> Pressure acts equally in all directions.

It is important to remember that in a liquid, the pressure acts equally in all directions and not just downwards. If you are swimming on your side in deep water, your 'bottom' ear will feel just as uncomfortable as your 'top' ear. A submarine will be experiencing pressure from all sides and not just downwards.

Dam walls are built thicker at the bottom to enable them to withstand the greater pressure found at the bottom of the reservoir.

You can see from the diagram that they do not need to be the same thickness at the top and indeed this would be an enormous waste of concrete - and money.

Fig.7.7

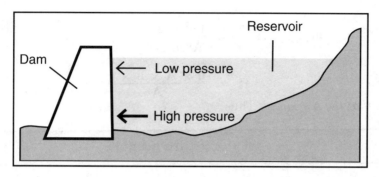

How Do We Calculate The Pressure In A Liquid?

Fig 7.8

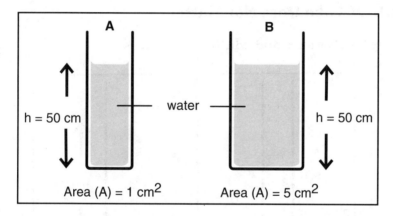

Pressure at the bottom of the tubes

$$= \frac{\text{Force exerted by the water (Weight)}}{\text{Area of the tube}}$$

Stage I: Finding The Force Exerted By Water (Weight)

	Density =	$\frac{\text{mass}}{\text{volume}}$

(i)   So,   mass (**m**)   =   density(**d**) × volume(**v**)

(ii)   volume   =   area (**A**) × height (**h**)

(iii) Force (**F**) [or weight of water]   =   mass (**m**) × gravitational force (**g**)

Using equation (iii):

          Force(**F**)   =   mass (**m**) × gravitational force (**g**)

*Substitute (**d** × **v**) for mass:*

          F   =   **(d × v) × g**

*Substitute (**A** × **h**) for volume:*

          F   =   **d × (A × h) × g**

Stage II: Finding The Pressure Exerted By The Water

$$\text{Pressure (P)} \quad = \quad \frac{\text{Force}(\mathbf{F})}{\text{Area}(\mathbf{A})}$$

So, $\qquad \mathbf{P} \; = \; \dfrac{\mathbf{d} \times \mathbf{A} \times \mathbf{h} \times \mathbf{g}}{\mathbf{A}}$

Notice that the A's cancel. Thus:

$$\mathbf{P} \quad = \quad \mathbf{d} \times \mathbf{h} \times \mathbf{g}$$

(This is a standard physics equation which you will come across much more in the future)

Width Of Tube Does Not Matter

Fig 7.9 Pressure and width of the tube

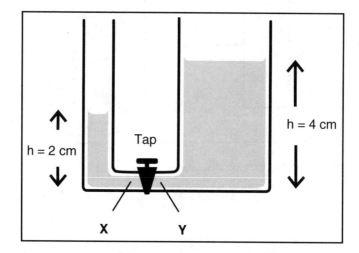

Looking at the tubes in figure 7.9, and the equations above, you can see that the pressure of the water at **A** will be the same as the pressure of the water at **B**, even though the tubes are of different width. The main thing to realise is that it is **density** and **depth** which determine the pressure at a particular point in a liquid.

PRESSURE AT X:	PRESSURE AT Y:
h = 2 cm	h = 4 cm
using, P = d × h × g	*using* P = d × h × g
P = 2dg	P = 4dg

Because there is a **Pressure Difference** between X and Y, **the water will move** until the pressure at X is the **same** as the pressure at Y.

This means that the expression **P= dhg** has to be the **same** for **both** sides.

We already know that **'gd'** is the **same** for both sides, so **'h'** (the height of the water) has to be the **same** in both arms of the U-tube.

This is what is meant by the expression 'liquids find their own level'.

This also explains why we can use, as a simple gauge, a clear, thin tube to tell the level of oil in an oil tank.

Fig. 7.10

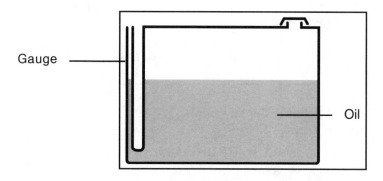

As there is no movement of the oil,
the pressure of oil in the gauge = the pressure of liquid in the tank.

Thus: $$h_{gauge} = h_{oil}$$

PRESSURE AND UPTHRUST IN LIQUIDS

We have already seen that bodies will float if the upthrust exerted by the liquid is more than the downward force (weight) exerted by the body.

The upthrust force exerted by a liquid was discovered by the Greek scientist **Archimedes**, who also discovered that the weight of water displaced by an object was equal to this upthrust force. This is known as **Archimedes' Principle**. In fact, it is not restricted to water, but applies to all liquids and gases (collectively called fluids).

> **Archimedes' Principle:** When a body is wholly or partially immersed in fluid, it experiences an upthrust equal to the weight of the fluid displaced.

Consider a body totally immersed in a liquid

Fig. 7.11

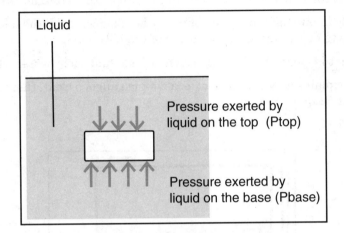

As P_{base} is **at a greater depth** than P_{top},
Then P_{base} will be **greater** than P_{top} .

So there will be a push upwards **(UPTHRUST)** which will be given by

$$UPTHRUST = P_{base} - P_{top}$$

This is why when you weigh an object in air, it will weigh **more** than when the same object is weighed when immersed in a liquid.

e.g.   a stone has a weight of 7 N when weighed in air. The **same** stone has a weight of 5 N when immersed in water

Thus, the **upthrust** exerted by the water, is   7 N – 5 N = **2 N**

APPLICATION OF LIQUID PRESSURE - HYDRAULIC MACHINES

If you look closely at a JCB digging, you will see that the arms which carry the digging bucket are moved by pistons located at the sides of each arm. The arms are, of course, levers, but the forces needed to move these arms come from the pressure of the liquid inside the system of pistons and tubes known as a **hydraulic system.**

What Is A Hydraulic System?

In its most simple form, a hydraulic system consists of two pistons (rather like syringes which you will have used in the laboratory) connected by a tube. The whole system is **completely filled** with a liquid e.g. water or oil. It is absolutely vital that there are no air bubbles or leaks in the system.

An **EFFORT** force is applied to one of the pistons (sometimes called the **MASTER CYLINDER**). This force causes an increase in the pressure of the liquid and so the liquid exerts a pressure on the other piston. If this piston (sometimes called the **SLAVE CYLINDER**) is of a larger size than the master cylinder, a larger **LOAD** force is exerted.

Fig. 7.12

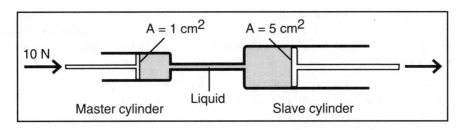

Looking at the MASTER CYLINDER

Effort Force   = 10N,   Area = 1cm², Pressure = ?

$$\text{Pressure} = \frac{\text{Force}(\mathbf{F})}{\text{Area}(\mathbf{A})}$$

$$= \frac{10 \text{ N}}{1 \text{ cm}^2}$$

$$= 10\text{N/cm}^2$$

So the Master Cylinder exerts a pressure of 10 N/cm² on the liquid.

Now, liquids have some important features:

    i) **they are incompressible;**

    ii) **changes in pressure are transmitted *instantaneously* to all parts of the liquid.**

> Thus, the liquid exerts a pressure of 10 N/cm² on the Slave Cylinder.

Looking at the SLAVE CYLINDER

    Pressure   = 10 N/cm², Area = 5 cm²,   Load Force = ?

$$\text{Pressure} = \frac{\text{Force}(\mathbf{F})}{\text{Area}(\mathbf{A})}$$

so,   Force   = Pressure × Area
              = 10 N/cm² × 5 cm²
              = 50 N

> Thus, a load force of 10 N on the Master Cylinder will cause an effort force of 50 N to be exerted by the slave Cylinder.

If there had been **two** Slave Cylinders, then a force of 10 N on the Master Cylinder would have resulted in forces of 50 N on **each** of the Slave Cylinders **at the same tim**e.

This has obvious applications in car braking systems.

As has been said before, it is vital, in all hydraulic systems, that all the pistons and tubes are completely **full** of liquid.

Any air bubbles in the system would cause it to fail, as air is compressible. This means that if an air bubble is present when a force is applied, the increased pressure in the liquid would merely squash the air bubble rather than push against the slave cylinder.

If there is an air bubble in a hydraulic system, all the liquid has to be removed (a process called 'Bleeding') and replaced with fresh liquid.

Pressure Exerted By The Atmosphere

Experiments to show that Atmospheric Pressure (A/P) exists

You will be familiar with the following:

1. Collapsing can: A metal can has a small quantity of water put into it and the can is then heated WITH THE CAP OFF. The water changes to steam which pushes air out of the can. After a time, it is considered that the air has been pushed out, so HEATING IS STOPPED and the cap is screwed on tightly. The can is now full of steam. As the can cools, the steam condenses back to water leaving nothing inside the can above the water - the air having been removed. A space with nothing in it is called a **vacuum**. Atmospheric pressure causes the can to collapse.

2. A glass full of water has a card placed on the top of it. The glass is inverted holding the card in place with a hand. When the hand is removed, the air pressure pushes against the card and holds it in place.

Why Is There An Atmospheric Pressure At The Earth's Surface?

Surrounding the Earth is the mixture of gases which make up our atmosphere. If you think of the upper limit of the atmosphere (about 80 km above the Earth) as the 'surface' of the atmosphere, then we on the Earth's surface are at the 'Deep End'.

As pressure in fluids (liquids and gases) increases as you go deeper, then it is clear that there is a pressure exerted by the atmosphere at the Earth's surface.

> Normal Pressure at sea level is usually taken as
> about 100 kPa ($10N/cm^2$)

Measuring The Pressure Of The Atmosphere

1. Aneroid Barometer('Aneroid' - without liquid).

The 'squashy' box is normally a flat, cylindrical, metal box with much of the air removed from it.

When **air pressure is high,** the **box is squashed** and **the top**, which is attached to a pointer by a system of levers, **goes down.**

When **air pressure is low**, the pressure on the box **becomes less** and the Return Spring, together with the small amount of air inside the box, causes the **top** of the box to **rise.**

This type of barometer can be made very small and it is this which is found in various guises, as found in small gifts.

Fig.7.13 Aneroid barometer

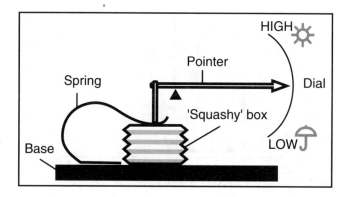

2. Mercury Barometer

You will know that mercury vapour is poisonous and so a mercury barometer, if it is made at all, is made only by a teacher who has taken precautions to ensure that any such vapour is unable to enter the laboratory atmosphere.

To make a mercury barometer requires a strong glass tube, about 80-100cm long, which is sealed at one end.

(i)   The tube is completely filled with mercury.
(ii) With the 'open' end sealed, the tube is inverted and the 'open end' is placed beneath the surface of mercury in a dish.
(iii)The seal is now removed from the 'open end'.
(iv) The mercury in the tube falls until the pressure at **X** (see fig. 7.14)is the same as the atmospheric pressure, pushing down on the mercury in the dish at **Y.**

The atmospheric pressure is given by the height of the mercury column **h**.

> Standard Pressure, when measured with this type of barometer, is 76cm of mercury

Above the mercury column there is almost a vacuum - in fact there is a very small pressure caused by evaporated mercury. This vacuum is called a **Torricelli Vacuum** after the Italian scientist Evangelista Torricelli, who first performed this experiment in 1664.

Fig. 7.14

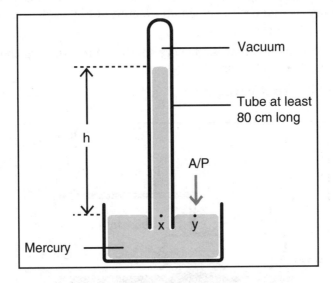

How Atmospheric Pressure Helps Us

Remember:

> There is no such thing as 'Suction' — A/P PUSHES.

1. Breathing

Breathing In (Inhaling):

The diaphragm is lowered, increasing the volume of the lung cavity. This lowers the pressure inside the lung cavity. Pressure of lung cavity is **less** than A/P and so A/P **pushes air into** the lungs.

Breathing Out (Exhaling):

The diaphragm is raised, decreasing the volume of the lung cavity. This increases the pressure inside the lung cavity.Now the pressure of the lung cavity is **greater** than A/P and is thus **able to push air out** of the body.

Fig 7.15

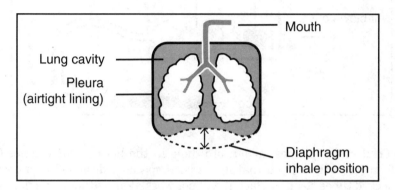

2. Drinking straw/ syringe

Fig 7.16

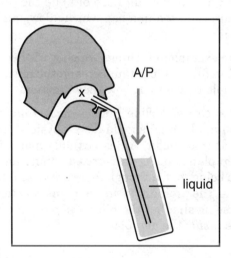

Pressure is reduced at **X**. Pressure at **X** is **less** than A/P, A/P pushes liquid up the tube.

3. Vacuum Cleaner

Fig 7.17

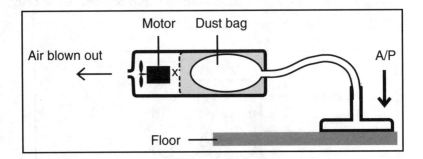

A powerful motor pushes air out of a hole in the back of the cleaner (some manufacturers will tell you that it has been specially designed as a device to blow blocked tubes clean - in fact, it will not work at all without this hole!). The pressure at X is reduced because of the removal of air by the motor. Pressure at X is less than A/P.

A/P Pushes air (and dust and small Lego bits) up the tube. The bits pushed up the tube by A/P are collected in a bag which allows air to pass through it, but not dust particles.

There are many more examples of 'Things which work' because of the pressure of the atmosphere, e.g. filling a fountain pen and the misnamed 'Suction Pad'. You should now be able to work out how they function.

Finally: Headlines such as "Airline Pilot is *sucked out* of the window of a Jumbo Jet at 15 000 m altitude" should, as a physicist, fill you with horror! You will know that at this height, A/P is virtually non-existant, but that the interiors of such aeroplanes have pressurised cabins for the comfort of the passengers. The idea being that, although there are large differences of pressure *outside* the aeroplane, the pressure *inside* remains constant, at a comfortable level. Which of course means that the pilot was *pushed* out of the window by the greater pressure *inside* the aeroplane.

What Do You Know About Pressure?

1. A block which weighs 12 N and has a base area of 2 cm², is standing on the floor.
(i) Write down the equation which you would use to measure the pressure exerted by the block on the floor.
(ii) What is the downward force exerted by the block?
(iii) What, in this case, does the word 'Pressure' mean?

2. The block has a weight of 0.6 N

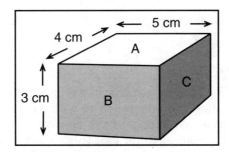

(i) On which face would you stand the block so that it exerts the **least** pressure?
(ii)If the block is stood on face C, what pressure would the block exert on the ground?

3. A box has a weight of 60 N. What pressure will it exert on the ground if the area of its base is:
(a) 10 cm², (b) 12 cm², (c) 0.06 m²?

4. A man has a mass of 75 Kg and the area of each of his shoes in contact with the ground is 250 cm².
(a) if the gravitational force is 10 N/kg, what is the weight of the man?
(b) What pressure does he exert when standing on: (i) both feet (ii) one leg?

5. A lady weighs 500 N and the area of one of her shoes in contact with the ground is 125 cm².
(a) What pressure does she exert when standing on both feet?
(b) If she is wearing stiletto heeled shoes and the area of one of the heels is 0.25 cm², what pressure does she exert if she puts all of her weight onto one heel?

6. A box weighs 100N and exerts a pressure of 25N/cm² when placed on a table. What is the area of the box in contact with the table?

7. Name **two** factors which determine the pressure in a liquid.

102

8. Explain the following:
   (a) A dam is thicker at its base than at the top.
   (b) Deep sea divers require protective suits.
   (c) It is quicker to fill a basin from a downstairs tap than it is from an upstairs tap.

9. Describe how you would show that the atmosphere exerts a pressure.

10. Explain **why** the atmosphere exerts a pressure at the Earth's surface.

11. What is the name of the instrument which is used to measure atmospheric pressure?

12. Explain with labelled diagrams, how the following work:
    (i)   a syringe;
    (ii) a vacuum cleaner;
    (iii) a bicycle pump.

13. (a) Draw a labelled diagram to help you explain how atmospheric pressure holds a rubber 'sucker' in place on a smooth surface.
    (b) Explain what would happen if the surface is rough.
    (c) Why would a physicist think that this gadget is 'misnamed'?

14. The diagram shows a mercury barometer.
    (a) Which height *a, b* or *c*, gives atmospheric pressure?
    (b) If a small hole was made at the top of the tube, what would happen?
    (c) What would be the height of the mercury if the tube had been **twice** as wide?

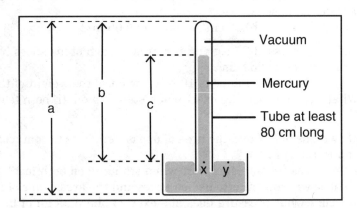

15. Describe, with the help of a labelled diagram, how an aneroid barometer measures atmospheric pressure.

16. The diagram below shows a simple hydraulic system. A force of 50 N is applied to piston A which has an area of 5cm².

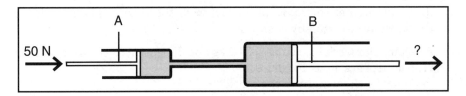

(a) What is the increase of pressure in the liquid caused by this force?
(b) If piston B has an area of 20 cm², what will be the force exerted by this piston?

Further Questions On Pressure.

1. Pressure in a fluid acts equally in all directions. Explain what this means, and give a way of demonstrating the truth of this statement.

2. **A** and **B** are filled with water. The density of water is 1000 kg/m³.
(a) What is the mass of water in **A** and in **B**?
(b) Is it true to say that the pressure on base **B** will be less than the pressure on base **A**? Explain your answer.

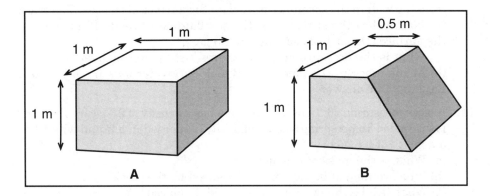

3. Explain why a diver experiences increasing pressure as he swims deeper below the surface of a lake.

4. The pressure at a certain depth of a fresh water lake is 200 000 N/m² higher than at the surface. What would be the pressure at the **same** depth below the surface of the sea?(*Assume density of fresh water is 1000 kg / m³; density of sea water is 1300 kg / m³*).

5. It is often said that "Water finds its own level". What does this mean? Draw a diagram of some equipment which demonstrates this effect. Describe briefly how it works.

6. A car weighs 12 000 N.
   (a) What is the force acting on each tyre, assuming that the car's weight is distributed evenly?
   (b) If the area of each tyre in contact with the road is 80 cm², calculate the pressure exerted by each tyre.

7. A rectangular block has a mass of 1.2 kg and dimensions 8 cm, 5 cm and 4 cm. (The force of gravity is 10 N/kg).
   (a) What is the weight of the block?
   (b) What is the area of the smallest face?
   (c) What pressure will the block exert if it rests on its smallest face?
   (d) What is the *least* pressure that the block can exert on the ground?

8. Describe, with the help of a diagram, a simple experiment showing how the pressure of a liquid varies with the depth below the surface of the liquid. Say what result you would expect to obtain.

9. A large metal can has a rubber bung fitted with a tube inserted into its opening. A vacuum pump is attached to the tube.
   (i) Explain what the pump does.
   (ii) Describe what would happen to the can.
   (iii) Explain why this experiment shows that the atmosphere exerts a pressure.

10. In a North Sea oilfield, some oil is seen floating on the surface of the sea. A diver is sent down to investigate a reported crack in the vertical pipeline from the well to the terminal located on the surface of the sea. The crack is 100 m below the surface and the sea barometer reads 10 m when at the surface.(Density of sea water = 1.3 g/cm³).
    (a) What is the pressure, in atmospheres, acting on the diver?
    (b) At the crack in the pipe, will oil leak out, water leak in, or neither? Explain your answer.

11. A block measuring 20 cm by 4 cm by 2 cm has a density of 2.5 g/cm³. The block is suspended from a spring balance and fully immersed in a liquid which has a density of 0.8 g/cm³.
    (a) What is the mass of the block?
    (b) What volume of liquid will be displaced by the block?
    (c) What will be the weight of the liquid displaced?
    What will be the reading on the spring balance when the block is immersed in the liquid?

12. The diagram shows a hydraulic jack. The area of piston **A** is 5 cm² and the area of piston **B** is 50 cm².
    If a force of 600 N is applied downwards at **X**, what force will be lifted by piston **B**? Show all working.

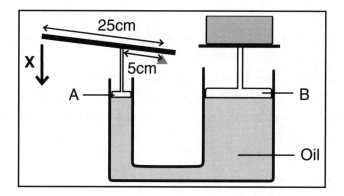

ENERGY

This is a very important topic as **everything** which happens requires a source of energy.

As the population of the World increases in size, so demands for a supply of fuels which release the energy which we require are increasing.

Because of this, energy is often confused with fuel - and they are **not** the same thing.

What Is Energy?

> Energy measures the size of a job that has been done.

Examples of jobs:

an animal moving, eating, living;
a kettle heating water;
a battery of cells making a 'Walkman' produce sound.

The size of the job (called **WORK**) can be measured and the unit of work is called the **Joule (J)**.

The unit is named after James Prescott Joule, born near Manchester in 1818, who first worked out that because temperature rose when work was done on a body, there was a relationship between energy and work.

In fact, 1J of energy is such a small amount that, for useful purposes, energy is often measured in kilojoule (kJ). [1000 J = 1kJ]

Although we cannot measure energy as such, we **can** measure the size of job (WORK) done.

We know that:

> The amount of work done = the amount of energy supplied

This equation will give us the **unit** which we use for energy.

In this equation, the unit on the left-hand side (WORK) is the joule,(J). This means that the unit for the right-hand (ENERGY) **must also** be the joule (J).

We say that:

> Energy is the ability to do work and is measured in joule (J).

How Can We Measure Work?

Work is done when a force acts on a body causing it to move a distance and is described by the relationship;

> WORK = FORCE applied × DISTANCE object moves*.

* The distance moved **MUST** be in the same direction as that of the force.

Fig 8.1

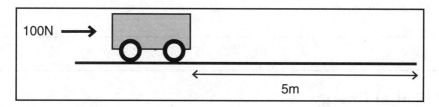

If a force of 100 N pushes a truck 5m, the amount of work done is given by :

WORK DONE = Force × Distance

= 100 N × 5 m

= **500 J**

This means that 500 J of energy was required (and supplied) to do the job.

Energy is given a different name depending on where it comes **from**, so we talk about different **forms** of energy.

> It is important to realise that the different forms of energy are the same, in that they all have the ability to do work

Their different names merely help us to know where the energy has come from.

Forms Of Energy

Kinetic Energy

Any moving body has kinetic energy. You know that you can hold a stone still against a window without causing any damage. If you throw the stone at the window, the stone will have enough energy to break the glass. Breaking glass is a job (even though it may not always be a useful one!) and requires energy. The energy for the job comes from the KINETIC ENERGY of the moving stone.

The amount of kinetic energy (KE) a body has depends on two factors:
  (i) the **mass** of the moving object;
  (ii) the **velocity** of the moving body (remember that velocity is a measure of speed in a particular direction).

The amount of kinetic energy which a body has can be calculated by using the expression :

Kinetic Energy(**KE**) = ½ of the mass(**m**) multiplied by the velocity squared(**v²**) and is usually written

$$KE = \tfrac{1}{2}mv^2$$

Potential Energy

This is energy a body has because of its **position or condition**.

(i) Gravitational Potential Energy

If you do a 'Bomb' jump from a diving board, you will make a bigger splash if you jump from a higher diving board. A large adult 'Jumper' will make a bigger splash than a smaller youth 'Jumper' when jumping from the same height.

When you jump, you will only fall downwards, because gravity pulls your mass.

Thus, the amount of gravitational potential energy which a body has depends upon:

  (i) the **mass** of the body;
  (ii) the **vertical height** which the body falls.

The amount of gravitational potential energy which a body has can be calculated by using the expression :

Grav. Potential Energy(**GPE**) = mass (**m**) × gravitational force (**g**) × vertical height which the body can fall (**h**) and is usually written

$$GPE = mgh$$

(ii) Elastic Potential Energy (Strain Energy)

You will know that if you wind up a clockwork toy, the more turns you make, the further/faster the toy will move.

In this case, the number of turns during winding is similar to the 'h' as seen in GPE.

If you pull back the string of a bow to shoot an arrow, the distance that you pull the string back (from its normal 'resting' position) is equivalent to the 'h' as seen in GPE.

Chemical Energy

When chemicals react they change. This change involves breaking the bonds which hold the atoms together and the forming of new bonds as new substances are made. Weak bonds between atoms occur because of a lack of energy, and so an input of energy (e.g. heating) is required to break them. It is the **formation of stronger bonds** which releases energy, sometimes in the form of radiation energy (heat, light), sometimes in the form of 'electrical' energy.
  e.g.
  (i) Burning magnesium will change chemical energy into radiation energy (heat and light).
  (ii) The chemicals of an electric cell will, when a circuit is complete, change chemical energy into electrical energy.

Electrical Energy

Electric currents move energy from one place to another. **When things move work is done** and so energy has been used. It is this energy which is used to make things happen e.g. a lamp shining or a motor turning, and this is sometimes known as 'electrical energy'. We shall use the term 'electrical energy' to describe the work done by an electric current.

Thermal Energy

All matter consists of molecules which are constantly in motion (i.e. have KE). If you add together the KE of all the molecules, you will have found what is known as the **Internal Energy** of the substance. If you add energy which is absorbed by the body - this is a process called heating - then the KE of the molecules will increase and thus the internal energy rises. This rise in internal energy can be detected by a rise in temperature.

So, the form of energy which brings about a rise in internal energy and hence, temperature of a substance, is known as **Thermal Energy** (sometimes this has also been known as Heat Energy).

Heating And Cooling

> • Thermal Energy always tries to flow a warm place to a colder one.
> • Bodies which absorb energy become warmer.
> • Bodies which "loses" energy become cooler

In Fig 8.2

A has more energy than **B**. Thus energy flows from **A** to **B**
A 'loses' energy, so becomes cooler.
B 'absorbs' energy, so becomes warmer.

Fig 8.2

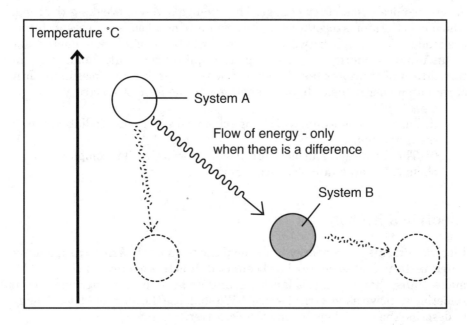

When **A** and **B** are at the **same** temperature, then there will no longer be an 'energy flow' in one direction.

e.g. If A is a cup of warm tea and B the surrounding air, then a warm cup of tea will 'cool' until it is the same temperature as the surrounding air (which will have warmed slightly).

If the air temperature is 20 ˚C then the tea (also at 20 ˚C) will feel cold when it enters a warmer mouth at 37 ˚C.

How Does Thermal Energy Move From Place to Place (Heat Transfer)?

There are **three** ways and each method depends upon the journey.

1. Molecules In 'Fixed' Positions - SOLIDS:
Energy travels by **CONDUCTION** rather like a 'Pass-it-on' game.

Fig. 8.3

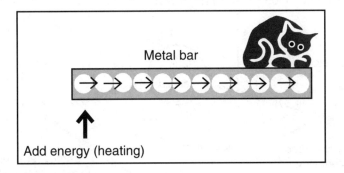

Thus:

> Materials which allow energy to travel through them are called **conductors**. Materials which do not allow energy to travel through are called **insulators**.

2. Molecules Moving Around Each Other - LIQUIDS/GASES:

Energy travels by **CONVECTION**.

As fluids become warmer, they expand. This means that the **same mass** of fluid has a **larger volume** and so the warm fluid becomes **less dense** and rises above colder, denser fluid, which sinks to take the place of the risen warmer fluid.

Fig. 8.4

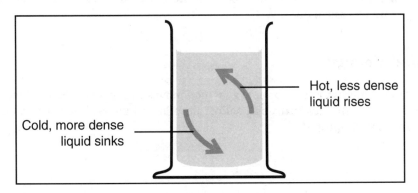

3. No Molecules At All - VACUUM:

Energy travels by **RADIATION.**
Bodies which give out radiation also absorb it and the important factor is the **surface** of the body.

Fig. 8.5

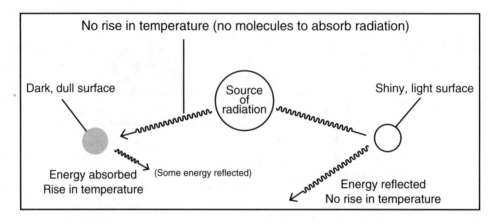

Radiation Energy

Energy from the Sun is carried by waves known as **Electromagnetic Waves.** The fact that the Sun's rays travel through all the emptiness of Space, tells us that electromagnetic waves **are able** to pass through a vacuum. There are many types of electromagnetic wave and these include:

infrared waves which will, if absorbed by bodies, cause them to heat up;

light waves which enable us to see objects (see chapter 9). Light waves are also absorbed by plants and provide the energy for the chemical reactions which change carbon dioxide and water into sugar and oxygen (photosynthesis);

ultraviolet waves which, when absorbed by some bodies, can be changed into light energy. Bodies which do this are called **fluorescent;**

radio waves which ,when absorbed by the aerial of a radio receiver, will change into electrical energy.

Sound Energy

Vibrating bodies will give out energy which moves in the form of sound waves. Sound waves will travel through solids, liquids and gases, but not through a vacuum (See chapter 10).

Nuclear Energy

Some forms of uranium consist of atoms which have energy stored within their very heavy nuclei. This energy is released when the nuclei are split apart (Nuclear **FISSION**) into fission fragments. Most of the energy released is kinetic energy of the fission fragments. These are slowed down in the material, raising its temperature. Heat is conducted from the hot **fuel rods** to the coolant fluid, which produces and superheats steam in a **heat exchanger**.

FUSION occurs with the nuclei of very light atoms (e.g. hydrogen) coming together - also with a release of vast amounts of energy. This is what happens on the Sun.

When nuclear energy is released in a careful and controlled way, it can be used to change water into steam at a Nuclear Power Station.

If a nuclear reaction is not controlled, then the nuclear reaction releases vast amounts of energy very rapidly - as in an atomic bomb.

Changing Energy From One Form To Another

When we say that we are using energy, we are really changing energy from one form to another.

e.g. a lamp changes electrical energy into thermal energy (i.e. the filament is heated until it is white-hot) and radiant energy (i.e. the white hot filament) gives out light.

Thus, if, 10 J of energy are used to light a lamp, we will not obtain 10 J,s worth of light, as much of the energy will be 'lost' in the form of heat as the lamp warms.

When energy changes form

> Total Amount of Energy at the Start   =   Total Amount of Enery at the End
>
> THIS IS KNOWN AS THE LAW CONSERVATION OF ENERGY

There are NO EXCEPTIONS to this law.

ENERGY DEGRADES AS IT CHANGES FORM

Let us look again at the light example .

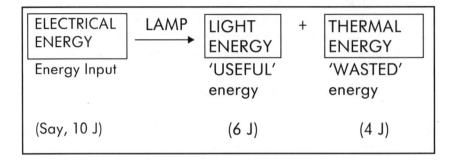

We know from the Law of Conservation of Energy that;

the ENERGY INPUT = ENERGY OUTPUT ('Useful' Energy + 'Wasted' Energy)

i.e. in our case,   10 J = 10 J   (6 J + 4 J)

But this law applies only to the **QUANTITY** of energy involved in the change of form. Another important factor which needs to be considered is that when energy changes form, the **GRADE** (or **QUALITY**) of energy **decreases**.

In this case, we could list the forms of energy in order of grade:

Electrical Energy - High grade

Light Energy

Thermal Energy - low grade.

In fact, **thermal energy is the lowest grade of energy and it is very difficult to use again**. It always appears at the end of all lists of energy changes, where it comes in the form of low-temperature energy radiating into the Earth's atmosphere warming it by a small amount.

So when your torch battery runs out, it is because the chemical energy which was stored in the cells of the battery became electrical energy when you switched on the torch. This electrical energy then ends up as light and thermal energy, which cannot be used again. Because you turned the torch on to be able to see in the dark, we are able to call the light energy 'useful' and the thermal energy 'wasted'.

Always remember:

> **Energy is NEVER used up. It changes from one form to another and in doing so, "steps down the grade at each change".**

Where Does Energy Come From?

The Sun as our main supply of energy.

DAILY RADIATION - a Renewable Resource.

Most of the Earth's energy comes from the Sun. If we stand outside on a sunny day, we will become warmer as the Sun's radiation causes an increase in our internal energy. This form of radiation can be collected and focused in one place, as in a **SOLAR FURNACE.**

Radiation from the Sun can also be changed into electrical energy by means of **SOLAR CELLS**. Whilst these have been very successful in providing energy for spacecraft, on Earth their use has been limited.

There are two reasons for this:

(a) there is a variation in the quantity of sunlight around the world - clearly Solar Cells would be more use in some parts of the world than in others;

(b) each cell only produces a very small amount of electrical energy and so a vast number of cells would be required covering a wide area.

e.g. you would need about 100 km^2 of solar cells to produce the same amount of electricity as a medium-sized power station (10 000 MW).

Light energy from the Sun enables plants to change carbon dioxide and water into sugars and starches (photosynthesis), which are a supply of chemical energy.

All living animals rely upon photosynthesis for their food, which provides their energy required for living and for the essential supply of oxygen - a 'waste' product of this reaction.

Because energy from the Sun is, for the forseeable future, continually radiated towards Earth, we say that light energy and thermal energy resulting from the Sun's radiated rays, are **Renewable** sources of energy.

FOSSIL FUELS - A Non-Renewable Resource

Between 100 and 600 million years ago, plants absorbed energy from the Sun and, through photosynthesis, 'stored' this energy in the form of sugars and starches. As plants died and fell into the swamps, so the chemical energy stayed 'locked' within them. Over a period of at least 100 million years these plant remains have become covered by layers of sediments. As more and more sediments were laid on top of the plant material, the pressure increased, and the plants hardened and became rock-like (**FOSSILS**), changing into **COAL.**

OIL was formed between 100 and 500 million years ago from small plants and animals living in the oceans. When they died, they sank to the ocean bed and were covered, as in the case of coal, with layers of mud and sediments. Over the following millions of years, the decomposed plants and animals changed into oil and gas. Thus coal, oil and gas are called **FOSSIL FUELS**.

They are sometimes called a **Primary** source of energy, because they do not become useful until the stored energy within them is released, by combining them with oxygen when they burn.

Fossil Fuels Are A Non-Renewable Energy Source

It takes over 100 million years to form coal, oil and gas and it is likely that we shall have used up supplies of these within a few hundred years. We must be thankful that we live at a time when there are adequate supplies of all three of these fuels and ensure that we use them wisely and make the supplies of them last for as long as possible. Apart from the benefits we receive by burning these fuels, there are many substances (plastics, medicines, cosmetics - to name but a few) which we are able to obtain from them. A world without oil does not merely affect the motor car!

Other Renewable Sources of Energy Resulting from Radiation from the SUN

Wind/Wave Energy

Radiation from the Sun causes some parts of the Earth to become hotter than others. This results in convection currents being set up in the oceans and atmosphere. These currents drive the winds and waves, thus changing the Sun's radiated energy into kinetic energy.

Falling Water Energy

Radiation from the Sun causes water to evaporate from oceans, rivers and lakes. The evaporated water rises by convection and is carried by winds and maybe falls as rain on high ground. Now, the water has gravitational potential energy. As the water falls back to the sea, its gravitational potential energy is changed to kinetic energy. This kinetic energy will enable the water to:
  (i)   wear away the mountainside - erosion;
  (ii) turn a water wheel - e.g. a flour mill;
  (iii) turn a turbine - hydroelectricity.

Energy from "Biomass"

A small amount (less than 1%) of the Sun's energy is absorbed by plants through the process of photosynthesis. This process changes simple chemicals (carbon dioxide, water) into complex ones (sugar,starches), thus increasing the size of the plant as these materials are stored within them. Thus, photosynthesis results in an increase of biomass - a supply of chemical energy. This supply of chemical energy can be used:

    (a) as a source of food - changed into thermal energy as animals do work;

    (b) in the production of fuel.

e.g. (i)   Wood - an important fuel.

      (ii) Production of methane - from rotting vegetation.

      (iii) Production of alcohol - from sugar plants which are allowed to ferment.

Renewable Energy Source From The Earth And Moon

Geothermal Energy

The temperature of the Earth's centre is about 4 000 ^{0}C. Thermal energy will be conducted towards the Earth's surface by rocks. Hot water from beneath the surface can be seen in places such as Iceland and New Zealand, where the Hot Springs, or Geysers, are used to heat houses.

Where there are no natural geysers, artificial ones (rather like oil wells) have to be drilled, and this, at present, is a very expensive process. However, as supplies of oil begin to run out, it could well be an alternative supply of energy to consider.

Tidal Energy

Rotational KE of the Earth, together with gravitational forces between the Earth and the Moon, cause the water of the oceans to be pulled into 'heaps' resulting in high tides about twice a day. Water which is trapped at high tide has gravitational potential energy and this can be changed into kinetic energy and used to turn turbines to generate electricity, as in Tidal Power Stations.

Nuclear Energy

(a) Natural Nuclear Reactions:

Within the Earth, there are certain substances which are unstable or radioactive. As the atoms of these substances break up, energy is released. This energy contributes to the maintenance of the high temperatures occurring deep within the Earth. These add to the geothermal energy which eventually flows to the Earth's surface.

(b) Man-Made Nuclear Reactions:

The breakup of nuclei of Uranium^{235} atoms releases energy which can be used to change water into steam. The steam is used to turn turbines to generate electricity.

Whilst a small amount of Uranium will produce a large amount of electricity, it is important to realise that Uranium is a non-renewable source of energy and supplies of this will, like coal, oil and gas, run out.

Power - Be careful how you use this word

You may have noticed that there was no mention of the word 'Power' in the descriptions of the various forms of energy e.g. wind power, wave power.

This is intentional as, like work, the word 'Power' has come to have many uses in our language.

However, it has a **special** meaning in physics.

We can express this as:

> Power is the amount of energy used in a certain time interval.
> **POWER (W) = Amount of Energy (J) / Time (s)**

The unit of power is the WATT (W) and so

> **1 W = 1J/s**

Thus, a 100 W light bulb uses 100 J of energy every second.

A Power Station is a place where electrical energy is generated and supplied at a rate of so many joule/second. Thus, a 100 MW Power Station (a small one these days) would provide a steady output of 100 000 000 J of electrical energy every second.

This may seem a large figure, but it will come into perspective when you set this agaadnst the total UK energy consumption of 10 000 000 000 000 000 000J (10^{19} J) for 1993.

Generating Electricity

When a coil (Rotor) turns inside a magnet (Stator) a current of electricity is produced.

e.g.

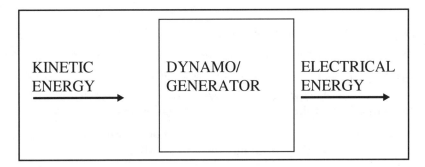

| KINETIC ENERGY | DYNAMO/ GENERATOR | ELECTRICAL ENERGY |

Methods Of Turning A Rotor

The coil (Rotor) is located on the same revolving axle as a set of turbines.

Fig 8.6

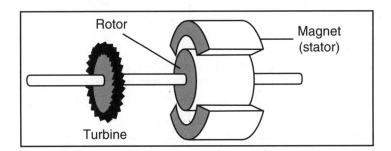

(a) Thermal Power Station

Steam at high pressure turns the turbines which turn the rotor. In order to change water into steam, water can be heated using coal, oil, gas or uranium.

(b) Hydroelectric Power Station

Water rushes at great speed past turbine blades which turn, causing the rotor to revolve.

What Do You Know About Energy?

1. Say what you understand by the term 'energy'.

2. (i) What is the unit of energy? (ii) Why is this unit so called?

3. Energy can be found as different forms. What have all the forms in common?

4. List five different forms of energy.

5. What does the Law of Conservation of Energy say? What does it mean?

6. (a) What do you think is meant by the following terms:
    input energy;   *useful energy;*   *wasted energy?*
    (b) What is the relationship between these terms?

7. What form of energy is always at the end of a sequence of changes when energy changes from one form to another?

8. List the energy changes which take place in the following:
    (a) A man diving from the high board into a swimming pool.
    (b) A television set showing a film.
    (c) An electric fire heating a room.
    (d) Singing into a microphone with a louder sound coming out of a speaker.
    (e) A steam engine winding up a 100 g mass from the floor to the benchtop.
    (f) A man walking up a flight of stairs.
    (g) A petrol engine moving a car.
    (h) A bow shooting an arrow into a straw target.
    (i) A Hydroelectric Power Station generating electricity.
    (j) A dynamo lighting the headlamp of a moving bicycle.

9. (a)What does the term **'Fossil Fuel'** mean?
    (b)Name two fossil fuels and say how they were formed.
    (c) Take **one** of your fossil fuels and say what energy changes are involved in its making and use.

10. (a) What does the word **'WORK'** mean?
    (b) What is the unit used to measure work?
    (c) State the relationship between work and energy.

11. It is possible to buy household electric lamps which are said to be more efficient than 'normal' ones.
    (a) Into what two forms of energy is the electrical energy changed   by a normal lamp?
    (b) If a lamp is more efficient, which of the energy forms is likely to be reduced?
    (c) If every house in the country used one new, efficient lamp,
    then at least one Power Station fewer would be needed. In what
     way might this be an advantage?

12. A cord is wrapped round the axle of a dynamo on a bench. A mass is tied to the cord and allowed to fall. The dynamo is connected to a lamp which lights as the mass is falling.
    What energy changes have taken place?

13. Conduction, convection and radiation are all words describing a method of transfer of thermal energy. Explain the meaning of these terms and give one example of each of them.

14. (a) Why do heated fluids rise?
    (b) Why does this not happen in solids?
    (c) Draw and label a diagram of some simple apparatus whichs h o w s this movement in a heated fluid.

15. Kinetic energy and potential energy are both forms of mechanical energy. Explain, giving examples, the difference between these two forms of energy.

16. Body temperature is 37°C and room temperature is 20°C. You stand barefoot with one foot on some carpet, the other foot on a stone floor.
    (a) Which surface is at the higher temperature - carpet, stone or neither?
    (b) Which foot will feel warmer? Give a reason for your answer.

17.

Activity	Energy required per minute
Sleeping	4kJ
Watching TV	5kJ
Eating	6kJ
Walking	12kJ
Swimming	30kJ
Playing Hockey	36kJ

(a) Make a sensible estimate of the amount of kJ of energy you would use over a 24 hour period if you are involved in all of the activities listed above.
(b) How would you replace the energy which you have 'used up' during the 24 hour period?
(c) Energy is never 'used up'. What has happened to it?

Further Questions On Energy

1. Outline the energy changes involved when the cars of a 'Roller Coaster' at a theme park are hoisted by an electric motor up the first hill to the start, and then are allowed to run freely up and down in a series of hills to the finish.

2. A ball has a weight of 5 N. It starts at rest at X, which is 3m above the foor, falls to the floor at Y and bounces up to Z which is 2 m above the floor.
    (a) Draw a diagram of the path of the ball X,Y,Z.
    (b) In what form is the energy of the ball :
          (i)   at X;
          (ii) at Y - *just before* the ball reaches the floor;
          (iii) at Y - when the ball is *not moving*;
          (iv) at Y - *just after* leaving the floor;
          (v)   at Z?
    (c) What has happened to the energy 'lost' by the ball between X and Z?

3. A horse, which eats hay and drinks water, is used to pull buckets of water out of a well. A rope attached to the horse goes round a pulley suspended over the well, and the bucket is attached to this rope. The water is 6m below the pulley and the horse has to exert a force of 500 N to lift one bucketful of water. The horse can lift 12 buckets of water in one hour.
    (a) How much work is done (i) to lift one bucket of water; (ii) by the horse after one hour?
    (b) When a bucket of water has been lifted to the top of the well, what kind of energy has it gained?
    (c) Explain where this energy has come from.

4. You have a bicycle fitted with a dynamo to drive the lamps. You freewheel down a hill and measure your speed at the bottom of the hill (a) with the lights switched on, and (b) with the lights switched off.
    Would you expect to find any difference? Explain your answer.

5.

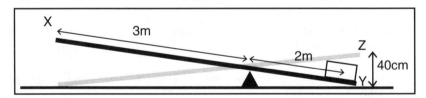

A man exerts a force of F N which lifts a load of 600 N from Y to Z.
At Z, the load falls off the plank and returns to Y
Calculate:
(a) the gravitational potential energy given to the load as it is raised to Y;
(b) the force (F N) exerted by the man;
(c) the work done by the man;
(d) the kinetic energy of the load as it arrives back at Y.

6. A man lifts a 400 N load onto the trailer of a lorry 1.5m from the ground.
(a) What is the gravitational potential energy gained by the load?
(b) If the load is pushed up a 4m ramp, what will be the gravitational potential energy of the load this time?
(c) What force will he need to exert to push the load up the ramp?
(d) Why will the man use more energy by pushing the load up the ramp, rather than lifting it directly onto the trailer?

For questions **7, 8, 9,** use the following information:
Power(WATTS) = Energy transferred(J) / Time (s);
There are approximately 3 ×10⁷ seconds in a year;
1 kilowatt-hour (kWh) is the energy transferred when a 1 kW appliance runs for 1 hour.

7. How much energy (in J) would a 1kW appliance transfer in
(a) 1 second;   (b) 1 hour;   (c) 1 year?

8. (a) How much energy would a 40 W light bulb transfer in one minute?
(b) If you leave a 60 W light on for 10 hours, how much energy do you transfer (i) in J, (ii) in kWh?
(c) If the cost of electricity is 7p for each kWh, how much will it cost to leave a 60 W light on for 10 hours?

9. A motor is said to have an output power of 2000 W.
(a) Explain what this means.
(b) How much work does the motor do in 1 minute?

10. An experiment was done to find out which of two mugs made of different materials would keep soup hotter for a longer time. Both mugs were filled with the same quantity of hot water and the temperature was noted every two minutes as they cooled down.
The mugs, P and Q, are the same size, but are made of different materials.

RESULTS

Time / min	0	2	4	6	8	10	12	14
Temp of P / "C	80	74	69	64	60	57	53	40
Temp of Q / "C	76	66	58	51	46	41	38	55

(a) Plot graphs of temperature against time for P and Q on the **same axes** on graph paper.
(b) One mug is made of polystyrene, the other of aluminium. Which is which? Give a reason for your answer.
(c) Explain why the graphs are not straight lines.

11. Night storage heaters are plugged into the electricity supply and during the night they warm up using cheap-rate electricity. During the following day, they slowly give out their 'stored' thermal energy to warm the room. Below are some suggestions for materials to fill such heaters. In each case, the heating element will be embedded in the material mentioned. Comment on each of the suggestions.
(i) It should be filled with cotton wool to keep the energy in.
(ii) It should be filled with dense material like bricks to store the greatest quantity of thermal energy.
(iii) It should be all made of metal, so that the thermal energy will flow out of it easily.

12. Double glazing consists of two sheets of glass with a narrow gap, in which there is air, between them.
(a) Explain how such a window reduces the flow of thermal energy.
(b) Why is such a window an advantage in summer as well as in winter?

13. (a) The Earth receives thermal energy which has been radiated from the Sun. Explain how we know that energy cannot travel from the Sun to the Earth by means of conduction or convection.
(b) Describe the best type of surface for an object if it is to be heated by the Sun's rays. List two other types of surface and explain why these surfaces would be poor for this use.

14. (a) Describe what you would do to show that hot air rises in a room.
(b) Why is the icebox of a refrigerator placed near the top?
(c) Why are radiators in a room usually placed on the floor under a window?
(d) Explain the parts played by conduction and convection, when an ice cube is placed in a drink to cool it.

15.   A heated house loses thermal energy as follows:

Walls	35%
Roof	?
Windows	10%
Draughts	15%
Floors	15%

(a) What percentage is lost through the roof?
(b) What accounts for the greatest loss of thermal energy? Suggest how this may be reduced.
(c) Why does the roof lose more thermal energy than the floor?

16. Architects use U-values to calculate the loss of thermal energy from a house.

They use the following equation to calculate loss of thermal energy:

Thermal energy lost per second (W) = U-value × area (m^2) × temperature difference.

Material	U-value
Roof, no insulation	2.0
Roof, insulated	0.4

(a) An uninsulated roof measures 10 m by 10 m. If the inside temperature of the house is 20°C and the outside temperature is 5°C, how much energy is lost through the roof (i) per second, (ii) per day?

(b) What is the energy saving per day if the roof is insulated?

Longer 'Essay Type' Questions

17. Many of todays economic problems stem from the high cost of energy. However there is a plentiful supply of energy around us (wind, waves, sunlight etc). Discuss why there is a problem over energy resources.

18. It has been proposed that we should develop and use nuclear fuel to provide most of our energy needs.

(a) How could people reduce their personal energy consumption, so that the need for nuclear fuel might be lessened?

(b) Is it better to reduce energy consumption or to build more nuclear power stations? Give a reasoned argument for your opinion.

ABOUT LIGHT

We see objects because light energy activates the receptors found in the **RETINA** of our eyes.

The light energy entering our eyes comes from one of two sources.

1. Luminous Source

Some objects, for instance, the Sun, a light bulb and a television set, give out their own light.

2. Reflection From Non - Luminous Objects

Most things, for example, a book or a table, do not give out their own light, but we can see them because light from a luminous source is reflected into our eyes.

> Light is a form of energy which is carried by transverse waves.

What Are Waves?

If you drop a stone into a still pond, ripples **(waves)** will move out from the splash to the edge.

Note: It is NOT the **water** moving outwards. If this were the case, then all the water would pile up at the edge of the pond.

If you put your hand in the water and move it up and down, you are producing a disturbance **(vibration)** in the water.

The disturbance will move outwards from the vibration in the form of waves - i.e. the waves are transferring the energy of the vibration.

The waves are called **TRANSVERSE** because they move **at right angles** to the direction of the disturbance (vibration).

Fig. 9.1 Transverse waves

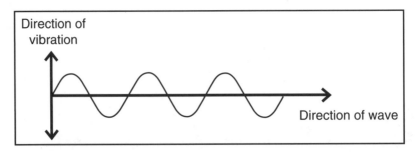

Features of Waves

Fig. 9.2

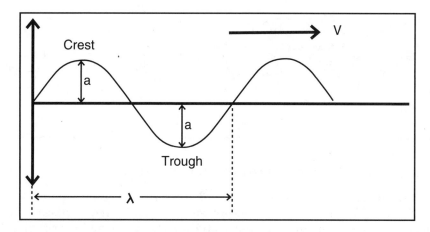

Wavelength (λ) (metre)

This is the distance between any two specified points of a wave. The distance can be the length between two crests, two troughs or, as in the figure, two points where the movement is upwards away from the horizontal mid-point.

Amplitude (a) (metre)

This is half the distance between a crest and a trough. The bigger the disturbance, the bigger is the amplitude of a wave.

Speed (v) (metres/second)

This refers to the speed that a point on a wave moves forward.

Frequency (f) (Hertz)

This is the number of waves passing any point in a second.

Electromagnetic Waves

These are waves caused by electrical **and** magnetic disturbances which combine to form electromagnetic waves.

There are many types of electromagnetic wave. Each one is of a different (and particular) wavelength. The various electromagnetic waves are listed, in size of wavelength order, in what is called the **electromagnetic spectrum.**

Fig. 9.3 Main features of the Electromagnetic Spectrum

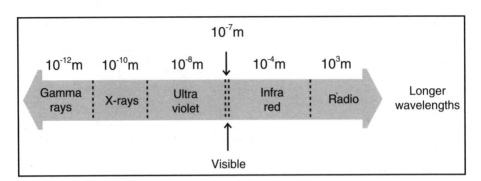

Some facts about electromagnetic waves

(1) They **all travel at the same speed** through a vacuum whatever their wavelength. They are very fast - at present, nothing is known to travel faster - and their speed through a vacuum is 300 000 000 m/s (usually written as 3.0 × 10⁸ m/s).

(2) They travel **in straight lines.**

(3) They, like all waves, **transfer energy** from one place to another.

(4) They can be **absorbed** and **emitted** (radiated out) by matter.

Light waves (rays)

1. The light may be **REFLECTED** i.e. it 'bounces off' the surface.

2. The light may be **REFRACTED** i.e. as the light ray passes through the material, it changes direction. This change of direction is called refraction.

3. The light may be **ABSORBED**. This fact becomes very important when we consider the colour of objects.

Fig 9.4

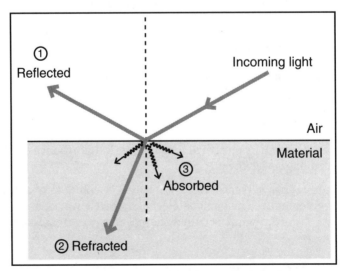

1. Reflecting Light

Some terms to understand first:

Incident ray - this is the light travelling **towards** the reflecting surface.
Reflected ray - this is light travelling **away** from the reflecting service.
Normal - this is an imaginary line at right angles to the reflecting surface.
Plane reflecting surface - a flat, smooth, shiny surface - as found on a plane mirror.

The Law of Reflection

The angle of Incidence   =   The angle of Reflection

Fig 9.5

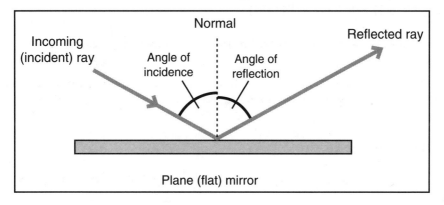

Using Mirrors To Reflect Light

1. Seeing behind you. A mirror on the handlebars of your bicycle enables you to see the road behind you - just like the driving mirrors on cars.

2. The Periscope. This is a tube which has two mirrors. Light from the object to be viewed is reflected from the top mirror onto the bottom mirror and into the eye. The tubes can be of various lengths. A long tube will be used in a submarine periscope, whilst a short one will be used in a **'hand held'** periscope to look over the heads of crowds.

Fig 9.6 Periscope

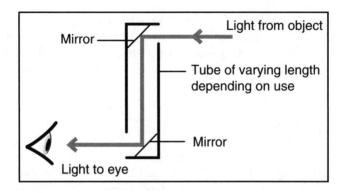

SCATTERING LIGHT in all directions (also called DIFFUSE REFLECTION)

Most objects are not smooth like mirrors, but have rough surfaces -like the page of this book.

When light rays strike such objects, they are reflected away in **many** directions. We say that the light has been **scattered**.

2. Refracting Light

Light will travel at different speeds, depending on what it is travelling through e.g.

Medium travelling through	Speed of light
Air	3.0 10^8 m/s
Water	2.25 10^8 m/s
Glass	2.0 10^8 m/s

When light travels **from air into water, it slows down** and **bends**. In fact, it will bend **towards** the normal.

Fig. 9.7

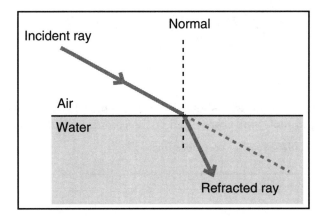

When light travels **from water into air**, **it will speed up** and bend. This time it will bend **away** from the normal.

Fig. 9.8

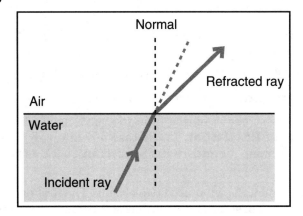

This is why the bottom of a swimming pool looks closer than it really is and why a stick appears to bend when it is partly submerged in water.

Fig. 9.9

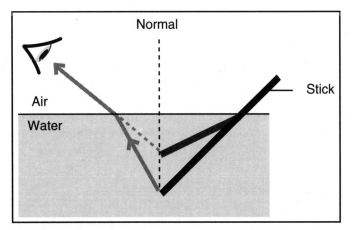

3. Absorbing Light

If a surface does not reflect or scatter light - rather like the printing ink on this page - that object will appear black.

Colour

It was Sir Isaac Newton who showed that the white daylight by which we can see objects is, in fact, a mixture of all of the colours of the rainbow.

Fig. 9.10 Newton's experiment

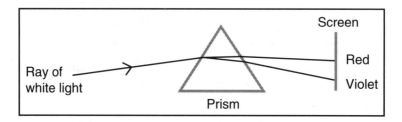

On the screen could be seen all the colours of the rainbow with the colours in the following order:

Red - Orange - Yellow - Green - Blue - Indigo* - Violet (purple)

* Indigo is hard to distinguish as it is a 'bluish black'.

The display on the screen resulting from the splitting of white light into its colours is called a **SPECTRUM.** In the case of white light, the colours run into each other forming a **continuous spectrum** - such as you can see in a rainbow.

In another experiment, Newton used two prisms. The first one split light into its several colours. These colours were passed through a second prism and were reconverted into white light.

Fig 9.11

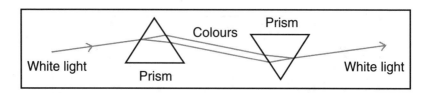

These experiments proved that white light (as in daylight) was indeed a mixture of lights of different colours and it is this fact which enables us to see coloured objects.

Remember:

> We only see objects because light is reflected from them into our eyes.

Colours And Absorption Of Light

Fig. 9.12

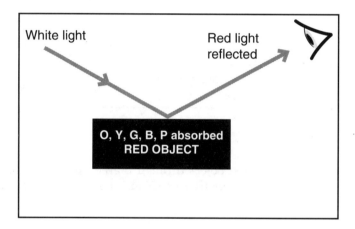

In this example, the orange, yellow, green, blue and purple light has been absorbed by the object and only the red light is reflected into our eye. This is why the object appears red.

Also;

Blue objects reflect **BLUE** light and absorb red, orange, yellow, green and purple light.

Green objects reflect **GREEN** light and absorb red, orange, yellow, blue and purple light.

Remember:

> An object appears **white** if it reflects **all** the colours.
>
> An object appears **black** if it reflects **none** of the colours.

Colour Filters

These are made from glass or plastic. Extensive use of colour filters is made in theatres to create various dramatic effects on stage. The filters are usually mounted on frames which clip onto the front of normally 'white' stage lights.

Colour of filter	Colours Absorbed	Colours Emerging
Red	Yellow, green, blue, violet	Red (+ some orange)
Green	Red, orange, blue, violet	Green (+ some yellow)
Blue	Red, orange, yellow, green, violet	Blue (+ some violet)

When Is A Red Object Not Always Red?

If you looked at the same red object through a green filter, the filter would absorb the red light. This means that no colour at all reaches your eye, thus the object appears black.

Fig 9.13

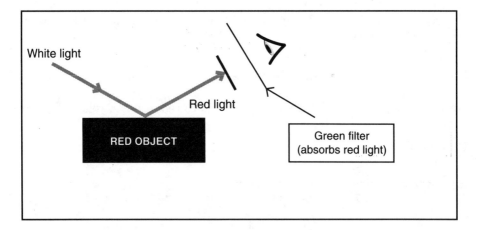

What Do You Know About Light?

1. What is meant by the term luminous source? Give three examples of luminous sources.

2. A table can be described as a non-luminous source and yet we can see it. Explain how this is possible.

3. Light is energy which is moved by transverse waves.
   Draw a labelled diagram of a transverse wave and show on your diagram:
   (a) the direction of disturbance;
   (b) the direction of the wave;
   (c) a wavelength;
   (d) the amplitude of the wave.

4. What is meant by the frequency of a wave and what unit is used to measure frequency?

5. Light energy is carried by electromagnetic waves which travel at 3×10^8 m/s. Describe three other facts about electromagnetic waves.

6. Draw a labelled diagram to show what happens when two parallel rays of light are reflected off a plane mirror.

7. Write the word **'FIRE'** as it will be written on the front of a fire engine. Explain why it will be written this way.

8. Using two mirrors, design an instrument for looking over a high garden wall. Say what your instrument is called.

9. (a) What is refraction of light?
   (b) Draw a labelled diagram of a ray of light travelling from air to water.

10. A coin is placed in a cup and you move your head until you cannot see the coin. A friend pours water into the cup and, without moving your head, the coin comes into view. Draw a labelled diagram and explain what is happening.

11. Why does a red object appear red in daylight? Draw a labelled diagram to help you explain.

12. What is a colour filter? Explain your answer and say what a green filter does.

13. (a) This page appears white - why?

(b) How can you make this page appear blue?

14. (a)What material do you think that a bicycle 'reflector' is made from? Give reasons for your choice.

(b) A reflector has the following pattern.

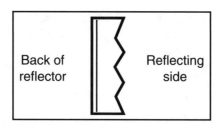

Draw a diagram which shows light from a car headlamp falling on the reflector.

ABOUT SOUND

Fig. 10.1

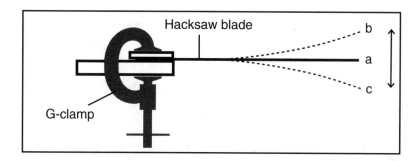

A hacksaw blade clamped to a bench (position *a*), is pulled upwards (position *b*) and released.

Because the blade is made of springy material, it will vibrate and the end will move through the following positions in turn:

$$b - a - c - a - b - \quad \text{and so on.}$$

The energy of the vibrations is carried through the air as **LONGITUDINAL SOUND WAVES**.

When these waves meet our ear drum, similar vibrations are set up in our ear. Thus we hear the sound of the vibrating hacksaw blade.

Thus;

> Sound waves carry energy away from a vibration.

SOUND WAVES

Look at figure 10.1.

(i) As the blade moves from *b* to *c*, the air beneath the blade is **squashed** - this part of the vibration is called **COMPRESSION.**

(ii) As the blade moves from *c* to *b*, the air beneath the blade is **stretched** - this part of the vibration is called **RAREFACTION.**

In this way, sound waves are made up of sequences of **COMPRESSION - RAREFACTION - COMPRESSION** ...and so on.

Fig. 10.2

If the blade is pulled further from (*a*), you would, correctly, expect the sound to be louder.

The distance from *a* to *b* is called the **displacement** and this gives rise to the **AMPLITUDE** of the sound wave.

> The greater the amplitude, the louder the sound.

Fig. 10.3

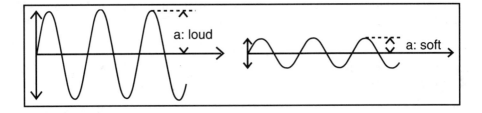

The number of times that the blade completes a vibration i.e. moves through a complete sequence of   *b - a - c - a - b*, is called the **FREQUENCY.**

If you used a **shorter** blade and pulled it up to (*b*), then the frequency of the vibration would be greater, i.e. the blade would vibrate more quickly. This would result in the production of a '**higher**' note or, more correctly, a note of a higher pitch.

The frequency of vibrations affects the Pitch of a sound.

> High Frequency results in sounds of high pitch
> Low Frequency results in sounds of low pitch.

As for light waves, the frequency of sound waves is measured in Hertz (hz).

The "Frequency Spectrum"

10 Mhz ULTRASOUND	Used in medical diagnosis
1 Mhz	Heard by some animals - a bat's radar
20 kHZ SONIC FREQUENCIES	Able to be heard by the human ear
20 Hz	
0 SUBSONIC FREQUENCIES	Vibrations from earthquakes

SOUND WAVES

Fig 10.4

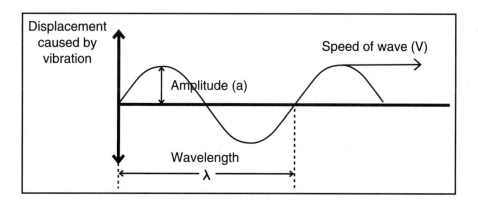

As sound waves are produced by squashing and stretching a substance, they are **only** able to travel through substances which contain atoms and/or molecules.

Thus;

> Sound waves **cannot** travel through a **vacuum.**

Speed Of Sound Waves

The speed of sound waves depends upon the material (**MEDIUM**) through which they travel.

MEDIUM	SPEED m/s
Gases (air)	330
Liquids (water)	1500
Solids (metal)	5000

Even so,

> **Sound waves travel much more slowly than light waves.**

MEDIUM	SPEED m/s
Light Waves in air	3.0×10^8 (300 000000)
Sound Waves in air	3.3×10^2 (330)

This is why, at a sports meeting, the timekeeper presses his stopwatch when he **sees** a puff of smoke from the starting gun and not when he **hears** the gun.

Why Do Sounds Become Fainter With IncreasingDistance?

The vibrations send out sound waves in **all** directions. This means that the sound waves spread energy over a **wider area** the further they are from the vibrating source. So the energy of the vibrations which the ear receives becomes less.

This explains why we can see cars moving along a distant motorway, even though we cannot hear them.

REFLECTION OF SOUND WAVES - ECHO

If you lay a long,weak, spring (e.g. a 'Slinky') flat on a bench, fix the far end and move the near end forwards and backwards, you will see the compression and rarefaction points move down the 'Slinky'. When they reach the far end, these points 'bounce' back down the slinky towards you.

This is just like sound waves travelling towards a wall and bouncing back towards you. If the wall is far enough away, the sound which you made will be heard again as an **echo**.

SONAR (ECHO-SOUNDING) - a method of finding out what is below a ship at sea

For this purpose, a beam of very high (inaudible) frequency sound waves (ultrasound) is sent out and the time taken for them to bounce off the seabed, or an object, is recorded very carefully.

e.g. *A ship sends out a sound wave to the seabed and receives it 0.5 seconds later. If the speed of sound in water is 1 500 m/s, how deep is the water?*

Fig. 10.5

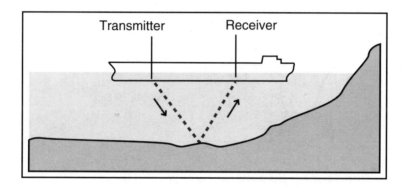

If it takes 0.5 s for the sound to travel to the sea bed and back, it will take 0.25 s to travel to the sea bed.

$$S = 1\ 500 \text{ m/s}, t = 0.25 \text{ s}, d = ?$$

$$S = \frac{d}{t}$$

Then, $\qquad d \quad = S \times t$

$$= 1\ 500 \text{ m/s} \times 0.25 \text{ s}$$

$$= 375 \text{ m}$$

So, the depth of the water is 375 m.

How We Hear Sounds

Sound waves cause the eardrum to vibrate.The vibrations are transmitted to the oval window by three connecting bones, **Hammer**, **Anvil** and **Stirrup** (**OSSICLES**) which act as levers.

Fig. 10.6

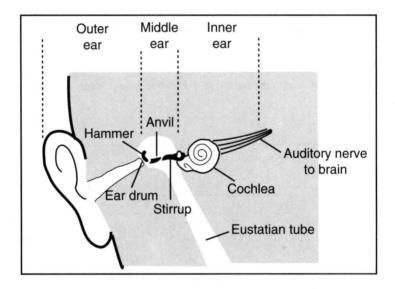

As the eardrum is larger than the oval window and because of the action of the levers, the vibrations on the eardrum will be magnified over twenty times by the time they reach the **oval window**.

The oval window is the receiving end of the **Cochlea** which is filled with liquid and lined with sensory cells connected to the **Auditory nerve**. Vibrations set up by the ossicles on the oval window are detected by the sensors in the cochlea and passed via the auditory nerve to the brain.

The **Eustachian tube** is normally closed and only opens to let air in or out of the middle ear when there is a change in pressure on the ear drum - e.g. when going up rapidly in a lift or aircraft.

'Popping' sounds in the ears are caused by the Eustachian tube opening when yawning or swallowing.

What Do You Know About Sound?

1. How are sound waves produced?

2. Will sound waves travel through a vacuum? Explain your answer.

3. The speed of sound in air is less than the speed of sound in a solid (e.g. iron). Explain why this is so. [Hint: think of molecules.]

4. A sound wave consists of points of high pressure (compression) and low pressure (rarefaction). Draw a diagram of a longitudinal sound wave and label these areas.

5. What feature of a sound wave determines the (i) pitch, (ii) loudness, of a sound?

6. (a) Describe how you would make a length of string produce a musical note.

   (b) How would you make the note higher?

   (c) How would you make the note louder?

7. The speed of sound in air is about 300 m/s. If thunder is heard 10 seconds after the lightning is seen, how far away is the storm?

8. What does 100Hz mean.

9. A man fires a gun and hears the echo from a building 550 m away. If the speed of sound in air is 330 m/s, how long after firing the gun will he hear the echo?

10. A Sonar pulse took 2.2 s to return to the sending ship sailing in water 650 m deep. What was the speed of the Sonar pulse?

ELECTRICITY I: Electrostatics

I - Electrostatics

We have already seen that bodies can be 'charged' in such a way that they are able to exert forces on other bodies.

As the charge remains in one place, we call this type of electricity - **STATIC ELECTRICITY.**

Where Does Static Electricity Come From?

All substances are made from atoms which contain **equal numbers** of positive charges (**Protons)** and negative charges (**Electrons**).

The protons are located in the nucleus of the atom, whereas the electrons are scattered around the nucleus in orbits.

Fig. 11.1

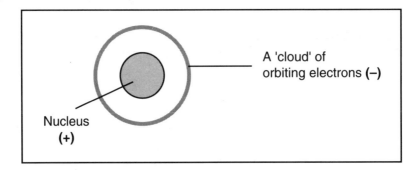

When a material, such as polythene, is rubbed with a woollen duster, some of the outer layer of electrons are removed from the duster. These electrons move onto the polythene.

The duster **loses** electrons and so now has a surplus of positive charges resulting in the duster becoming **positively** charged.

The polythene **gains** electrons and so now has a surplus of negative charges resulting in the polythene becoming **negatively** charged.

Note that:
   (i) Rubbing only *separates* the charges.
   (ii) The *protons remain* where they are; it is the *electrons which move.*

Before you rubbed the polythene strip with the duster, the strip is said to be **uncharged.**

In fact it would have contained charges, but the positive and negative charges would have been in **equal** quantities.

> **An uncharged** body has **equal** number of **positive and negative charges.**

> A **negatively** charged body is one which has **gained** electrons and **so has more electrons** than protons.

> A **positively** charged body is one which has **lost** electrons and **so has more protons** than electrons.

How Electric Charges Behave

You will remember that:
Similar charges repel
Unlike charges attract
Charged bodies attract uncharged bodies

How Do Charged Bodies Attract Uncharged Bodies?

In fig 11.2 (a), the uncharged ball has **equal** numbers of positive and negative charges.

In fig 11.2 (b), negative charges in the body are **repelled** by the approaching negatively charged rod and so move further into the ball. This leaves a **surplus** of positive charges on the surface nearest to the approaching rod.

The positive charges on the body are now attracted towards the negatively charged rod and so the ball moves towards the rod.

Fig. 11.2

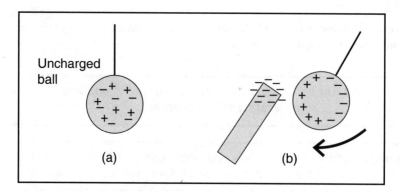

(a)   (b)

If the body *touches* the rod, some of the negative charges from the rod will move onto the ball giving the body a surplus of negative charges.

When this happens, the now negatively-charged ball will jump away from the negatively-charged rod.

The Electroscope

An electroscope is an instrument used to detect the presence of electric charge. The hinged flap is usually made from gold leaf (*very thin* sheets of gold), so the instrument is often called a **Gold Leaf Electroscope.**

Fig 11.3

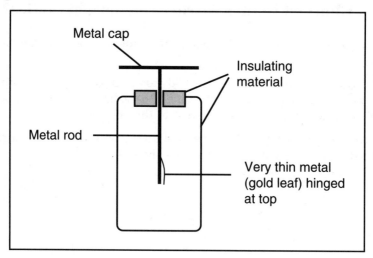

Using An Electroscope

Fig. 11.4

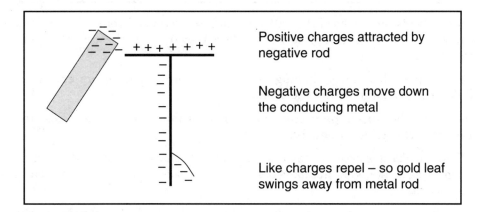

Positive charges attracted by negative rod

Negative charges move down the conducting metal

Like charges repel – so gold leaf swings away from metal rod

When the charged rod is removed, the charges move back to their original position and the gold leaf falls back.

Why Does A Charged Balloon Stick To A Wall?

Rubbing a rubber balloon on a woollen jumper causes the balloon to become negatively charged.

Fig. 11.5

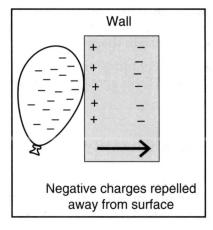

Wall

Negative charges repelled away from surface

As the negative charges near the surface of the wall are repelled by the approaching negatively-charged balloon, a surplus of positive charges remain at the wall's surface.

So the balloon (negatively charged) is attracted to the now positively-charged surface of the wall.

Large Amounts Of Static Electricity

> Lightning: A familiar spectacular example of static electricity.

Storm clouds tend to be of the 'tall' type and convection currents within them carry small droplets of water upwards where they freeze in the upper layers of the cloud.

The ice particles move, rubbing against each other, setting up enormous difference of charge within the cloud.

As a rule, the **upper part** of a cloud carries a **positive** charge, whilst the **lower part** carries a **negative** charge.

When the charges become too great, a sudden discharge occurs in the form of a lightning strike. Vast numbers of negative charges (electrons) are moved in an instant.

As well as releasing light energy (lightning), the discharge also heats the surrounding air to a high temperature very quickly. This rapid expansion of air produces sound - which we call thunder.

Lightning discharges can take place between clouds, within the cloud itself, or between the cloud and the ground.

Lightning striking the ground delivers an enormous amount of energy in a very short time and so damage to trees and buildings may occur. When lightning strikes a tree, the huge quantity of thermal energy causes the fluids (sap, water) within the tree to boil instantly and so the tree 'explodes'.

In order to protect buildings, a **lightning conductor** consisting of a metal rod with a sharp point at the top, is fixed to the tallest part. This rod is connected to a thick copper strip running down the outside of the building to a long metal rod (or metal plate) buried in the ground.

The metal point attracts the lightning strike and the electrons travel down the connecting strip to the rod. This spreads the charge around in the earth. The building is thus protected.

Man-Made Charges In Quantity - The Van de Graaff Generator

The charge is taken to a dome, which is situated at the top of an insulated column, by a moving insulated belt (usually rubber).

The charge is collected by a metal 'comb' at the top, which conducts it to the outside of the dome. You will learn later in your physics studies that charges collect around the outside of hollow conducting bodies such as spheres or metal cans. So, as more charges are brought up by the belt, they collect in large quantities on the outside of the dome.

Fig. 11.6

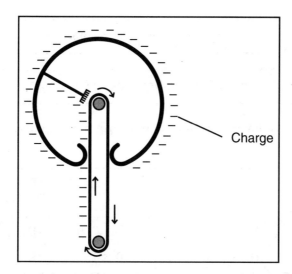

Charge

If an uncharged sphere, which is connected to earth (**earthed**), is brought near to a charged Van de Graaff dome, the charge which has built up on the dome will 'discharge' - rather like lightning - and a spark will be seen to jump the gap.

On **moist** days, charge from the outside of the dome will 'leak' into the atmosphere and that is why you will either have only seen a Van de Graaff operating on a dry day, or your teacher will have dried the machine and the surrounding air with a hair drier.

CONDUCTORS - CURRENT - FLOW OF CHARGE

When 'earthing' a Van de Graaff generator, the charges (electrons) which have collected on the dome, flow through the conducting material to earth.

The **moving electrons** are an ELECTRIC CURRENT.

CONDUCTORS and INSULATORS

All Metals are conductors.

Conduction involves Moving Electrons.

Fig.11.7 Structure of metals showing arrangement of atoms

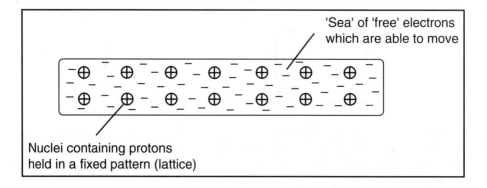

'Sea' of 'free' electrons which are able to move

Nuclei containing protons held in a fixed pattern (lattice)

Fig. 11.8 Structure of an insulator (e.g. plastic) showing arrangements of molecules

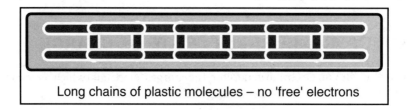

Long chains of plastic molecules – no 'free' electrons

What Do You Know About Electrostatics?

1. There are two types of electric charge. Electric charges exert forces on each other.Describe the forces that occur between:
    (a) two negative charges;
    (b) two positive charges;
    (c) a positive and a negative charge.

2. Describe how you can show that there are two types of electric charge.

3. What is meant by the term 'uncharged' when applied to a body?

4. (a) How can you show that a plastic ruler becomes charged when it is rubbed on a woolly garment?
    (b) When a polythene rod is rubbed with a duster it also becomes electrically charged. How could you find out if the charge on the polythene rod is the same as the charge on the ruler from (a)?

5. A lightning conductor consists of three main connected parts.
    Draw a labelled diagram of a lightning conductor and explain the reasoning behind its design.

6. (a) Draw a labelled diagram of a gold leaf electroscope.
    (b) Explain how it can be used to show if a body is charged.

7. A rod, which is positively charged, is brought towards a conducting ball hanging on a thread.
    (a) What is the first behaviour of the ball as the rod approaches?
    (b) What is likely to happen after the rod has touched the ball?

8. Six conducting balls are hung from a horizontal bar by nylon threads. They are numbered one to six and ball six is negatively charged.
    One at a time, each ball is unhooked, carried by its thread and placed close to each of the remaining balls. The following observations are made:

    (a)   Ball 1 attracts Ball 3
    (b)   Ball 1 attracts Ball 4
    (c)   Ball 2 repels Ball 6
    (d)   Ball 3 repels Ball 2
    (e)   Ball 4 attracts Ball 3
    (f)   Ball 5 repels Ball 4
    Say, with reasons, whether each of the balls one to five is positively charged, negatively charged, or uncharged.

9. (a) Explain how a Van de Graaff Generator builds up such a large amount of charge.
    (b) Where does the charge collect?
    (c) Say what conditions produce poor results when using a Van de Graaff Generator and why.

10. A metal rod will conduct electricity, whereas a plastic rod will not. Explain the difference in the way the particles (atoms, molecules, electrons, protons) are arranged in these two materials, allowing the metal to conduct electricity whilst the plastic does not.

ELECTRICITY II: Current Electricity

Charge On The Move

We have seen from the previous chapter that when there is a difference in the electric charge between two ends of a conductor, then electric charge will flow through the conductor in the form of electrons.

The fact that electrons flow at all shows that there is an energy difference between the two ends of the conductor.

Consider a water analogy:

Fig. 12.1

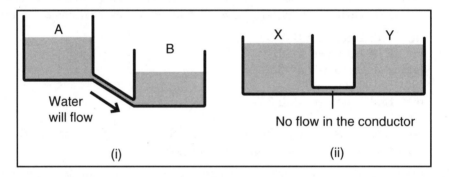

In fig. 1(i), the water has greater potential energy at **A** and so flows to **B**, whereas there is **no flow** in fig. 1 (ii) as X and Y are at the **same** energy level.

In fig. 1(i), **A** represents the positive terminal of a battery or cell and **B** the negative terminal.

Beware! Water Analogies Have Limitations

(a) Electric current does **not** run downhill - think of the switch in the wall which turns the ceiling light on/off.
(b) If there was a gap in the water pipe, all the water would drain away. If there is a gap in an electric circuit, **NO CURRENT FLOWS AT ALL**.

Electric current moves **from the +** (*positive*) terminal through the circuit, **to the -** (*negative*) terminal of a cell/battery.

This is known as the **CONVENTIONAL FLOW OF CURRENT**. It was agreed by scientists before they knew about electrons.

Clearly, electrons, being negatively-charged, will flow towards the positive terminal of a cell/battery.

Even so, we say that

> **Current flows from positive to negative**

even though the electrons are, in fact, going in the opposite direction.

Drawing Electric Circuits - A Reminder Of Some Of The Symbols Used

Fig 12.2 Circuit Symbols

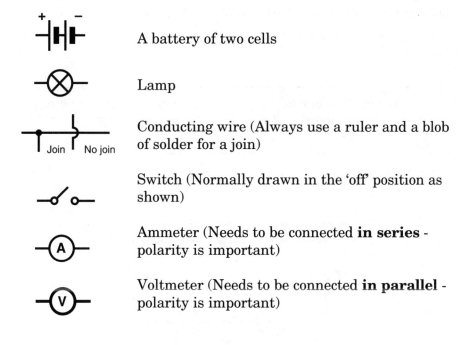

A battery of two cells

Lamp

Conducting wire (Always use a ruler and a blob of solder for a join)

Switch (Normally drawn in the 'off' position as shown)

Ammeter (Needs to be connected **in series** - polarity is important)

Voltmeter (Needs to be connected **in parallel** - polarity is important)

Series Circuits

These are so called because there is only **ONE** path for the current to travel and the current flows through each component in turn - i.e. one after another.

Fig. 12.3

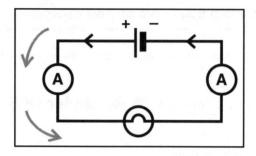

The lamp glows with 'normal' brightness and **both** ammeters read 0.2 A.

This circuit shows that **current is NOT used up** as it goes round a series circuit and that

Amount of Current leaving the positive terminal of the cell	=	Amount of Current entering the negative terminal of the cell

Fig. 12.4

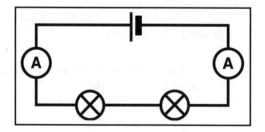

Both lamps glow 'dimly' and **both** ammeters read 0.15 A.

Fig 12.5

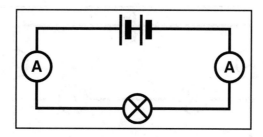

The lamp glows 'brightly' and **both** ammeters read 0.3 A

Summary Of The Circuits In Figs. 12.3,12.4 and 12.5

1.   If number of cells = number of lamps   – the lamps are of
                                                               'normal' brightness.
       If number of cells > number of lamps   – the lamps are 'bright'.
       If number of cells < number of lamps   – the lamps are 'dim'.
2.   BRIGHT lamps show that a LARGE CURRENT is flowing.
       DIM lamps show that a SMALL CURRENT is flowing.

Parallel Circuits

Fig. 12.6

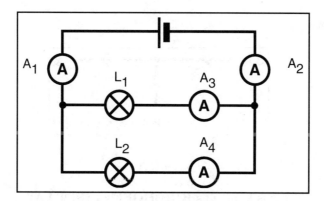

Try to think of this as **TWO CIRCUITS,** each of one cell, and one lamp, which
are connected to, and supplied by, the same single cell.
Circuit 1: Lamp (L_1) is 'normal' and ammeter A_3 reads 0.2 A.
Circuit 2: Lamp (L_2) is 'normal' and ammeter A_4 reads 0.2 A.
Ammeter A_1 will read 0.4 A (0.2 A for lamp L_1 + 0.2 A for lamp L_2)
Ammeter A_2 will read 0.4 A (0.2 A from lamp L_1 + 0.2 A from lamp L_2)
Thus, two lamps, if connected in parallel, can be lit to 'normal' brightness
by one cell.

Fig 12.7

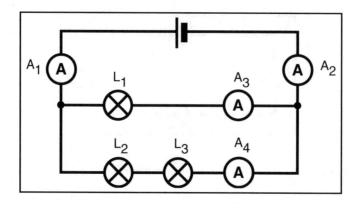

Circuit 1 (1 cell, 1 lamp): L_1 is 'normal' and A_3 reads 0.2 A.
Circuit 2 (1 cell, 2 lamps): L_2 and L_3 are both 'dim' and A_4 reads 0.15 A.
Ammeter A_1 reads 0.35 A (0.2 A from L_1 + 0.15 A for L_2 and L_3)
Ammeter A_2 reads 0.35 A (0.2A from L_1 + 0.15 A from L_2 and L_3)

Current At A Junction

When there is a junction in a circuit, the current divides such that:

> The total current entering the junction = the total current leaving the junction.

Fig 12.8

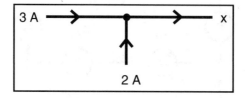

$$x \quad = 3\,A + 2\,A$$
$$= 5\,A$$

(This is known as **KIRCHOFF's FIRST LAW**)

Cells/Batteries

A cell produces an energy difference between its two terminals as a result of a chemical reaction.

The energy difference (called **Potential Difference**) is measured in **volts** (**V**). The unit is called after Alesandro Volta, who invented the first cell in 1794.

Fig. 12.9

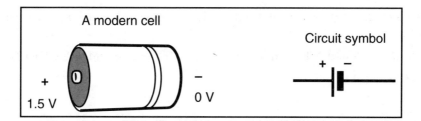

The maximum potential difference which can be produced as a result of a chemical reaction, is about 2 V. So, if an energy difference of more than 2 V is required, this is possible by adding cells together.

The 'usual' cell which you will have used in your laboratory experiments has an energy difference of 1.5 V. Thus a 6 V battery (of cells), will be four 1.5 V cells added together (all facing the same way).

Why Do Cells Run Down?

We know that current is not used up in a circuit, so what is?

The answer is ENERGY!

You already know that energy is not 'used up' but becomes changed (transformed) into other forms of energy. Finally, at the end of the 'transformation chain', thermal energy is radiated out into the atmosphere.

The energy comes from the chemical energy stored in the cell. This energy is carried by the current and transformed by the lamp into light energy and thermal energy.

Fig 12.10

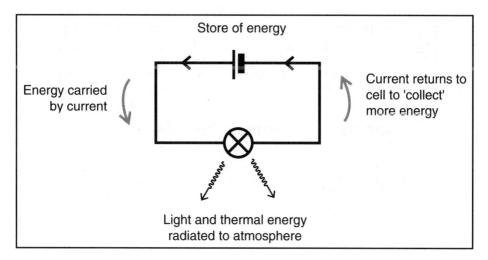

If a lamp is brighter, or a fire is hotter, energy will be radiated to the atmosphere at a faster rate.

You have already seen that brighter lamps mean that a larger current is flowing.

So, LARGE CURRENTS run cells down QUICKER than SMALL CURRENTS.

Fig. 12..11

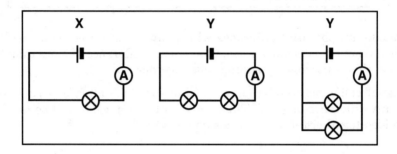

In X: Lamp is 'normal brightness, ammeter reads 0.2 A.
In Y: Both lamps are dim, ammeter reads 0.15 A
In Z: Both lamps are at 'normal' brightness, ammeter reads 0.4 A
As the current is **greatest** in Z, the cell in this circuit will **run down first**.

Resistance To Current Flow

Fig. 12.12

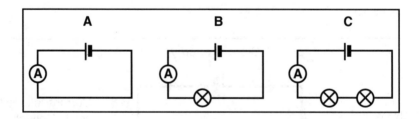

CIRCUIT	AMMETER READING
A	> 1.0 A
B	0.2 A
C	0.15 A

The reduction in the current is caused by *'more things being in the way'* of it. We say that the lamps are **offering resistance** to the current.

> **Increasing resistance → reduces current.**

The amount of resistance can be measured and is recorded in **Ohms** (Ω).

This unit is named after **George Simon Ohm** who, in 1826, discovered that there was a mathematical relationship which defined the Potential Difference between the ends of a conductor and the amount of current flowing in it.

Resistors

These are components designed to reduce current in a circuit - or parts of it.

Types Of Resistors:

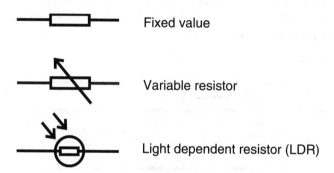

Fixed value

Variable resistor

Light dependent resistor (LDR)

Light Dependent Resistor (LDR)

The pair of arrows is a standard physics symbol which is used to show the passage of light. When light falls on an LDR, the value of its resistance falls. **In the dark, an LDR has high resistance**.

To help you remember how an LDR works, think of **L,L,L** !

> **An LDR has Low resistance in Light.**

Resistors Transform Energy (Also known as the Heating Effect of a current)

The act of resisting a current causes some of the electrical energy to change into thermal energy - in the same way that the force of friction changes movement (kinetic energy) into thermal energy.

Certain materials offer greater resistance than others.Copper, gold and silver are examples of **good conductors** of electricity, because they offer **low resistance** to current flow.

Tungsten and Nichrome (an alloy of Nickel and Chromium) are often used when heating by an electric current is required, because they offer substantial resistance and so heat up when a current passes through them.

Other Factors Affecting Resistance

1) Length of resistance wire:

Clearly, a long length of resistance wire will offer more resistance than a short one.

2) Thick or thin resistance wire:

Think of a three lane motorway. Traffic flows well, engines and passengers are nice and cool........until the cones!

Now, the *same* volume of traffic is trying to pass through a much *narrower* spot. The cones offer resistance to the traffic which slows down, resulting in engines and passengers warming up.

Fig. 12.14

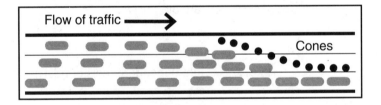

A thick wire offers less resistance than a thin wire.

3) Temperature Of A Resistor

As a resistor becomes hotter, the particles within it vibrate more and so the passage of an electric current becomes increasingly difficult.

When materials are cooled to very low temperatures, the movement of the molecules becomes less - providing an 'easier' path for the electric current - hence they become 'Super Conductors'.

The resistance of a wire increases as the temperature increases.

The Misnamed 'Short Circuit'

This is misnamed because it has **nothing to do with length.** Current will **always** take the **easiest route** (i.e. **with least resistance**) if it can.

Fig 12.15

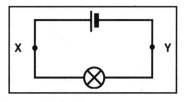

If a wire is connected between X and Y, the lamp will go out as most of the current will 'choose' to go through the **less resistant** connecting wire XY. Thus there will not be enough current flowing through the lamp to light it.

The route XY is called a Short Circuit.

Fig 12.16

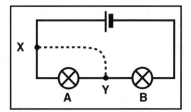

If XY is connected by a conducting wire, then lamp A is short-circuited by XY. Lamp A goes out and Lamp B becomes brighter (lamp B is effectively now part of a circuit comprising two cells, one lamp).

Using Resistors To Heat 'Things Up'

1. A Filament Lamp

Fig. 12.17

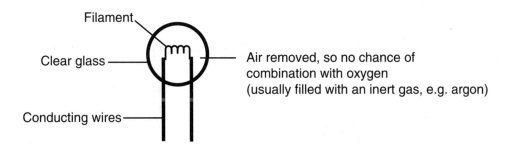

FILAMENT: Thin, high resistance wire, often tungsten, offers high resistance to the current. Thus, when a current flows, the wire becomes white hot, changing electrical energy into light energy and thermal energy.

2. Electric Heaters

Fig 12.18

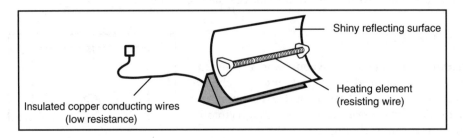

Shiny reflecting surface

Heating element
(resisting wire)

Insulated copper conducting wires
(low resistance)

3. Fuses

A fuse is a safety device put into a circuit to protect components from currents which are too large.

Fig. 12.19

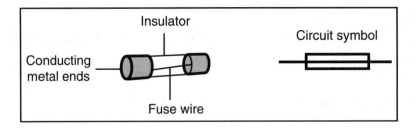

Insulator

Circuit symbol

Conducting
metal ends

Fuse wire

An electric motor works well when a current of 2 A is flowing, but would burn out if there were a current of 5 A in the circuit.

Fig 12.20

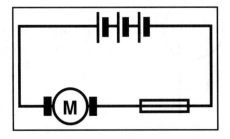

Putting a 3 A fuse (so called, because it is designed to 'blow' if the current is greater than 3 A) in the circuit would allow the motor to work well and also protect it from larger currents which could damage it.

What Happens When A Fuse Blows?

When there is a current in a circuit which is too large for a fuse, the fuse wire

> HEATS — MELTS — and BREAKS the circuit, stopping
> all current in th circuit immediately.

Making Magnets - The Magnetic Effect Of An Electric Current

In 1819, **Hans Oersted** discovered that when a current is present in a conductor, a magnetic field exists around the wire.

The magnetic field will have direction as shown by the movement of a compass needle if placed near to a wire having a current in it.

If the direction of the current is changed, the compass needle points in the opposite direction.

Fig. 12.21

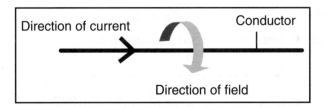

To remember the direction of the magnetic field, think of a screwdriver and screw.

As you screw **in** (i.e. *in the direction of the current*), you turn the screwdriver to the **right, in a clockwise direction** (this is the *direction of the magnetic field*).

If you bend the conductor in a loop, you will see from fig 12.22, that the direction of the field *inside* the loop is *out* of the page, towards you.

Fig 12.22

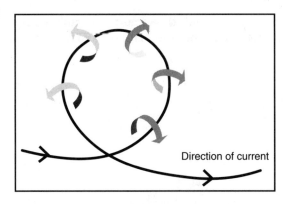

Now make *several* loops side by side - as in a **coil**. It is important to use insulated wire, so that the current runs the length of the coil wire and does not take short cuts where the turns touch.

You will find that there is a strong magnetic field *inside* the coil which:

(a) ceases if the current stops flowing;

(b) is in one particular direction;

(c) will reverse in direction if the direction of the current is reversed.

If a soft iron 'core' is placed inside the coil, this will become a magnet when the current is switched on.

Fig 12.23 A Solenoid

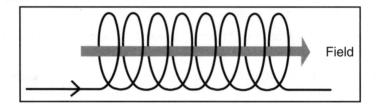

A Solenoid

A long coil of wire is also called a **solenoid.**

Fig 12.24 Circuit symbol for a coil/solenoid

The **strength** of the magnetic field **inside** a solenoid can be **increase**d by:

> a) increasing the number of turns of the coil;
> b) increasing the current;
> c) using soft iron core.

The Electric Bell

When the bell push is pressed, the circuit is complete. The coil becomes an electromagnet and attracts the iron armature causing the hammer to strike the bell.

Fig. 12.25

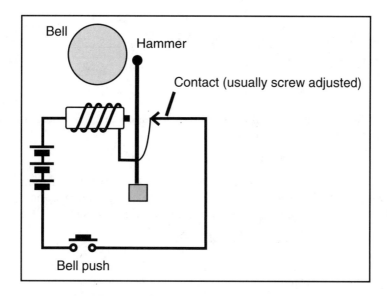

This movement of the armature breaks the circuit switching off the electromagnet. The spring pulls the armature back to its original position and so contact is made. The circuit is complete once more and the sequence begins again.

Michael Faraday 1791 - 1867

His interest in science was awakened whilst he was an apprentice to a book binder in London. During this time, he attended the lectures at the Royal Institution given by Sir Humphrey Davy.

Faraday took copious lecture notes and presented these, illustrated and bound, to Humphrey Davy who, in 1813, employed him as his assistant.

Davy was a chemist, so, much of Faraday's early work was in chemistry. However, Faraday became interested in electricity and magnetism and it is his discoveries in this area of physics for which he will be best remembered.

It was Faraday who found that if a conductor is in a magnetic field and a current is flowing, movement will result. This important discovery led to the development of the electric motor.

Faraday also revealed that if a coil of wire is made to turn inside a magnetic field, an electric current will be produced.

This is the principle behind the Dynamo (Generator).

Faraday was also a brilliant lecturer and began the Royal Institution Lectures for Young People. These lectures continue today, taking place around Christmas time. They are televised and are well worth watching - or better still, attending.

Fig. 12.26 The Principle of a Dynamo

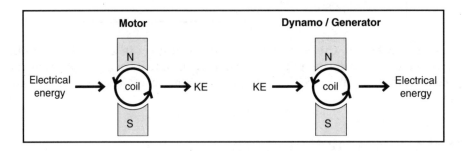

Diodes

Look carefully at fig 12.27 and notice that it makes a difference which way round a diode is put into a circuit. Diodes (sometimes made from silicon or germanium) belong to a group of materials called **semiconductors**. This is because they will allow current to flow through them one way, but almost no current to flow through the other.

Fig. 12.27

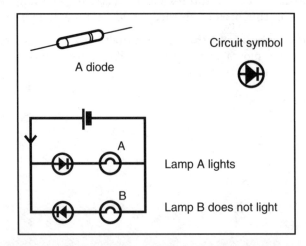

Fig. 12.28

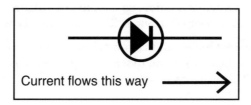

Current flows this way ———→

Using Diodes

Some components can be damaged if current flows through them the wrong way, so diodes are used whenever it is important to rely upon the direction of the current e.g. in radios and computers.

Fig. 12.29

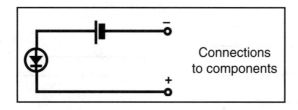

Connections to components

Light Emitting Diode (LED)

These are diodes which **emit light** when a **current flows** through them. LEDs can be damaged easily if too large a current flows through them, so a protective resistor is always connected in series with an LED.

Fig. 12.30   Light Emitting Diode (LED):   Circuit symbol

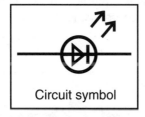

Circuit symbol

As you would expect with a diode, it is **vital** to connect it the right way round. The **positive** lead is called the **Anode**. The **negative** lead is called the **Cathode**.

Which Is Which?

Length of lead is not always a guide, so look at the coloured part of the LED. One side of the rim has been 'flattened'. **The flat side is the cathode (-).**

LEDs come in various shapes and colours. Red is the most widely used, but yellow and green are quite common too. For very special uses (these are much more expensive!), it is possible to obtain a blue LED.

Some More Switches

SPDT (Single Pole Double Throw)
Pole - refers to the conducting path **INTO** the switch.
Throw - refers to the conducting path **OUT FROM** the switch.

Fig. 12.31

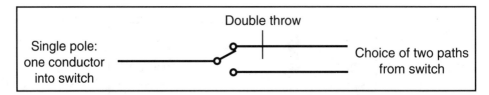

Push Switches

Fig. 12.32

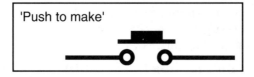

This means that the circuit is completed ('made') when the switch is pressed, e.g. calculator button, computer keyboard switch.

Fig.12.33

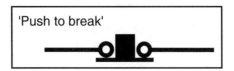

Contact is broken when the switch is pressed. e.g. Car doors closing would push the switch to turn off the interior lights.

Combining Push Switches

Switches In Series - A Simple 'AND' Circuit

We can summarise the results in a **Truth Table**. The **INPUT** being provided by the two switches A and B. The **OUTPUT,** in this case, is the lamp.

Fig 12.34 Switches in Series

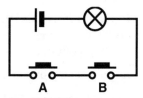

INPUTS		OUTPUT
Sw. A	Sw. B	Lamp
Open	Open	Off
Open	Closed	Off
Closed	Open	Off
Closed	Closed	On

The lamp is ON, only when switches A **AND** B, are closed.

Switches In Parallel - A Simple 'OR' Circuit

Fig. 12.35

Switches in parallel

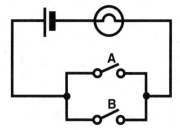

INPUTS		OUTPUT
Sw. A	Sw. B	Lamp
Open	Open	Off
Open	Closed	On
Closed	Open	On
Closed	Closed	Off

The lamp is ON, when switches **A OR B**, **OR BOTH**, are closed.
AND and **OR** circuits are examples of **Electrical Logic Circuits.**

Electrical Logic (Cause/Condition And Effect)

A logical statement: If it is raining, and I go outside, I will get wet.

This can be broken down into three separate parts, *two parts being conditions* and the *third being the result.*

CONDITION (INPUT)	EFFECT (OUTPUT)
(1) "It is raining"	
(2) "I go outside"	(3) "I will get wet"

For **each** of these parts of the statement, there are **two** possibilities.

Either YES (Logic 1) or NO (Logic 0).

In electrical terms:

Logic 1 refers to YES, there is a current flowing, (or *Logic High** indicating a Potential Difference is present).

Logic 0 refers to NO, there is not a current flowing, (or *Logic Low** indicating that there is no Potential Difference present).

* You will meet these terms later in your physics studies when you look at electronic logic and Potential Difference in more detail.

Thus,

Input 1: "It *is* raining" -logic 1;   "It is *not* raining" - logic 0
Input 2:"I *go* outside" - logic 1;   "I do *not go* outside" - logic 0
Output: "I *will* get wet" - logic 1;   "I *will not* get wet" - logic 0

All the possible combination of conditions (Inputs) and their outcomes can be summarised in the Truth Table below.

Note that there are **four lines** in the truth table. This is because there are **two** conditions, **each** capable of having **two** possibilities (Yes or No; Logic 1 or 0).

If there was only **one** condition, e.g. "It is raining", then there would be **two** lines in the truth table e.g.

INPUT	OUTPUT
0	0
1	1*

* Assuming that I am standing outside!

In General:

The number of lines (possibilities) in a truth table is given by 2^n

Where,   **2** represents the number of logic states (0 or 1)

          n represents the number of conditions

          and so on.

Number of Conditions (Inputs)	Number of Possibilities/ Truth Table Lines
1 2 3 and so on	$2^1 = 2$ $2^2 = 4$ $2^3 = 8$

Logic Gates

A gate is a device which, when open, may let animals in/out of a field and when closed does not. An electrical gate performs the same function in an electrical circuit.

Thus,

> Switches in series form an AND gate.
> Switches in parallel form an OR gate.

AND Gate

Fig 12.37 Logic symbol:(The symbol is based on the 'D' of AND)

Truth Table

INPUT		OUTPUT
A	B	
0	0	0
0	1	0
1	0	0
1	1	1

OR Gate

Fig 12.38 Logic symbol

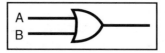

Truth Table

INPUT		OUTPUT
A	B	
0	0	0
0	1	1
1	0	1
1	1	1

Reed Switch

Fig 12.39 is both a symbol of the reed switch and what it actually looks like. Looking closely at the symbol will reveal how the switch works. The contacts are normally open and can be closed by the action of a magnet.

Fig. 12.39

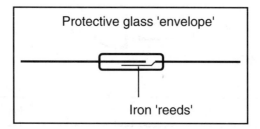

Protective glass 'envelope'

Iron 'reeds'

As a magnet is brought close, a process called **magnetic induction** causes the two reeds to become magnetised and they are attracted towards each other. When they touch, the circuit is complete.

Reed Relay

If a reed switch is placed **within** a coil, then when current flows through the coil, a magnetic field is created which closes the contacts.

Fig. 12.40

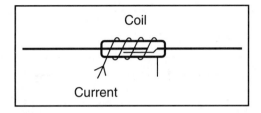

Such a device is known as a **reed relay.**

A relay is really a switch which is operated by an electromagnet and **consists of two separate circuits.**
Circuit I - a small current which is used to make the coil a magnet.
Circuit II - the 'end use' circuit - the currents in these circuits can be quite large.

Fig. 12.41 A car starter motor switch

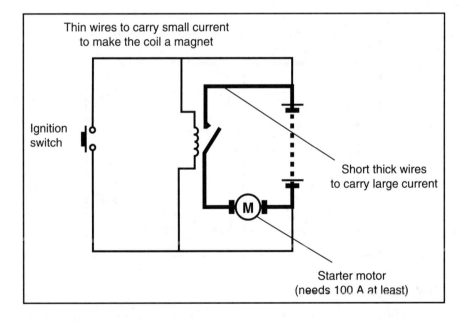

Using A Reed Relay

Imagine that you wish to make an electric motor turn on in the light and turn off in the dark.

A First Solution

Fig. 12.42

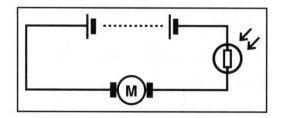

This will not work as the resistance of the LDR, even in the light, is too great to allow there to be a large enough current to operate the motor.

A Better Solution - Using A Reed Relay

Fig 12.43

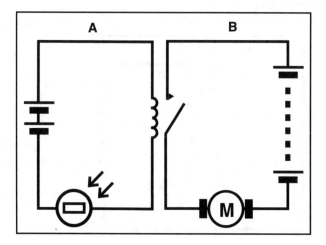

In the light:

LDR has *low resistance*, so coil becomes a magnet which closes the switch in circuit B and the motor works.

Notice that circuit **B** has a *minimal amount of resistance*. In circuit **A**, the LDR could be replaced by a switch, a water sensor, a heat sensor - the options are many.

What Do You Know About Current Electricity

1. Draw a circuit which contains a cell, a lamp and an ammeter in series.

2. For each part, draw a circuit which has one cell which will:
    (a) light two lamps to 'normal' brightness;
    (b) light two lamps equally dimly;
    (c) light two lamps equally dimly and a third lamp to 'normal' brightness.

3. One cell lights a lamp to normal brightness.
    Using the terms **dim**, **normal, bright** or **out**, say what you can about
    the brightness of the identical lamps in the following circuits:

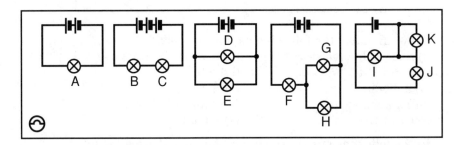

4. In the following circuit, both lamps are similar and the current at point
    B is 0.2 A.

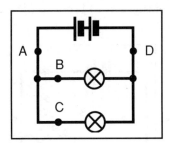

What is the current at (i) A, (ii) C, (iii) D?

5. In the circuits below, all lamps are similar.
   (i) In which circuit is the current leaving the cell the greatest?
   (ii) In which circuit will the cell run down quickest?

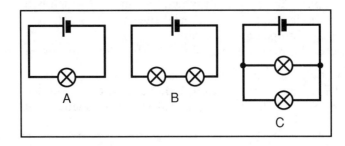

6. Draw and label the following circuit symbols:
   (i) fixed value resistor   (ii) a variable resistor
   (iii) an LDR   (iv) a fuse
   (v) a diode   (vi) a coil
   (vii) a push switch   (viii) an SPDT switch
   (ix) an LED   (x) a motor.

7. In the following circuit, the lamps A,B and C are all similar.
   (a) Will the brightness of lamps B and C be more than, less than, or the same as that of A? Give a reason.
   (b) A length of copper is connected between points P and Q.

What happens to the brightness of (i) lamp A, (ii) lamps B and C?

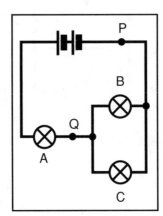

8. Explain what happens if you close the switch on the following circuits. You should comment on the brightness of the lamp/s and the ammeter readings.

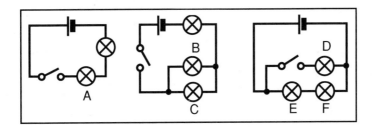

9. Which of the following lamps will be lit? Explain your answer.

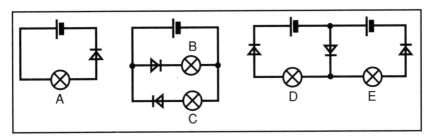

10. Four copper wires of the same length, but of different diameters, are connected in turn to complete a circuit containing an ammeter and a cell.
    The results are given below.

Diameter of wire / mm	14	8	10.5	4
Ammeter reading / A	0.8	0.2	0.45	0.05

(i) Draw a graph to show how the current in each wire varies with its diameter.
(ii)What can you say about the relationship between the current through the wire and the diameter of the wire?

11. (a) Explain why the wires which carry electric current to an electric fire need to be thicker than wires which carry the current from the battery of a pocket calculator.
    (b) The wire for the heating element of an electric fire consists of many thin strands rather than one thick strand. Why?

12. In the circuits below, all lamps and cells are similar.

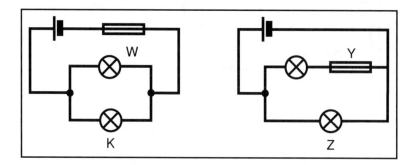

(i) In which circuit will the current through the fuse be greater?
(ii) Describe what happens to a fuse when it blows.
(iii) Describe what happens to lamps **W** and **K** if the fuse blows.
(iv) Describe what happens to lamps **Y** and **Z** if the fuse blows.

13. Look at the circuit below.

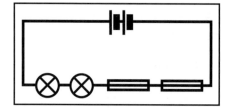

Say, giving your reasons, if it is true that the circuit needs two fuses because it contains two cells and two lamps.

14. Draw a labelled diagram of a cartridge fuse (such as may be found in a 13 A plug).

15. (a) Draw a circuit which has two cells, an ammeter and an LDR in series.
(b) This circuit was used to test how easily light shone through four different kinds of paper A,B,C and D. Each sheet was the same thickness. A lamp was shone on to the LDR and each sheet of paper was placed in turn between the lamp and the LDR. The reading on the ammeter was noted in each case with the following results:

Sheet of Paper	A	B	C	D	No Paper
Current / mA	23	17	21	19	38

(i) Why does placing paper between the lamp and the LDR change the current?
(ii) Which kind of paper was the least transparent?

16. (a) Describe how you would use a cell and some wire to magnetise an iron nail.
    (b)How would you use a small compass to show that the nail had become a magnet?
    (c) What could you do to make the nail a stronger magnet?

17. The Electrical Section of a Scientific Supplier's catalogue lists an item as a 'Motor/Dynamo'. Explain how this one item can perform either as a motor or as a dynamo.

18. Using one cell, two push switches and a lamp, draw:
    (i) a simple **OR** circuit;
    (ii) a simple **AND** circuit.

19. A table lamp has an 'on/off' switch on it. The lamp is plugged into the mains supply at a socket where there is also an 'on/off' switch.
    Say what type of circuit this is and draw a truth table for it (use: lamp switch, mains switch, lamp and logic symbols 0,1).

Further Questions On Current Electricity

1. In the circuit below, all lamps are similar.

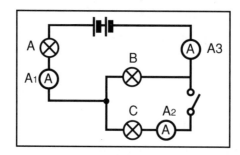

(a) With the switch open, ammeter A_1 reads 0.2 A. What would be the readings of ammeters (i) A_2, (ii) A_3 ?
(b) Say what you can about the brightness of lamps A, B and C when the switch is open.
(c) Say what you can about the brightness of lamps A, B and C and the readings of the ammeters when the switch is closed.

2. In the circuit below, lamps A and B are identical and the ammeter reads 0.2 A.

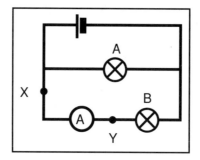

(a) What is the current in lamp A?
(b) What is the current in the cell?
(c) If a connecting lead were to be connected between X and Y, say what would happen:
(i) to lamp A, (ii) to lamp B,   (iii) to the ammeter reading.

3. In the circuit below, all lamps are similar and one cell lights a lamp to 'normal' brightness.

    Make a list showing whether each lamp in the circuit is bright, normal, dim or out.

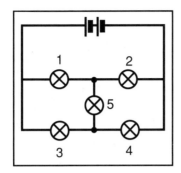

4. You are given four identical lamps A,B,C and D, four switches 1, 2, 3 and 4 and a cell which will light each of the lamps separately to normal brightness.
Draw a circuit in which:

Switch 1 lights lamps A & B at normal brightness;
Switch 2 lights lamps C & D equally dimly;
Switch 3 lights lamp D at normal brightness and prevents lamp C from lighting at all;
Switch 4 can turn lamp B off, but can only turn it on again if Switch 1 is on.

5. In these two circuits, all cells and lamps are similar.

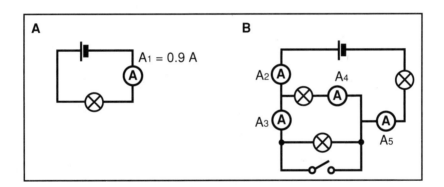

In circuit **A,** A1 reads 0.9 A. In circuit **B,** A_2 reads 0.6 A
(i) With switch **S** open, what do ammeters A_3, A_4 and A_5 read?
(ii) If switch **S** is closed, what do the ammeters A_2, A_3, A_4 and A_5 read?

6. (a) Draw a diagram of a circuit which contains: one cell, a diode, two lamps in parallel with each other.
(b) Mark clearly on your diagram:
(i) with the letter **S,** where you would place switches to operate each lamp independently;
(ii) with the letter **F** where you would consider the most suitable position for a fuse.
(c) Could the fuse be placed anywhere else in the circuit and still work? Explain your answer.

7. Electric current is a flow of electrons through a conductor. In the circuit below, all the resistors are identical.

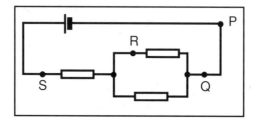

(a) In the circuit, 2 million electrons pass through P every second. How many electrons per second pass through (i) point Q, (ii) point R, (iii) point S?
(b) In the figure below, a steady current flows through a thick piece of wire AB which is joined in series with a thin piece of the same sort of wire BC. BC is half the diameter of AB.

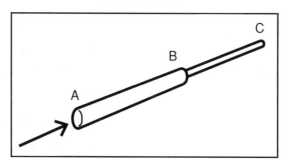

(i) If 2 million electrons pass any point in AB each second, how many must pass a point in BC each second?
(ii) If the electrons move down AB with an average speed of 0.4m/s, what is their average speed in BC? Explain your answer.

8. A thin piece of copper wire can safely be used to connect a lamp to a cell. Yet the same piece of copper wire when connected across a mains socket, would immediately cause a disaster. Explain what happens in each case and account for the difference.

9. In the circuit below, ammeter A$_2$ reads 0.4 A.
   What would you expect ammeters A$_1$ and A$_3$ to read?

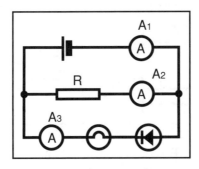

The resistor **R**, is made from a length of wire. What would you expect to happen to each ammeter reading if **R** were replaced by a resistor using half the length of the same wire.

10. Look at the circuit below and explain what happens for different combinations of switch settings and why such an arrangement of switches might be useful.

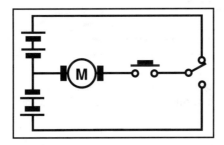

11. Draw a circuit to show how two push switches can be used as an AND gate with an LED indicating the logic state of the output.

12. When a torch is shone at a sensor a motor starts to turn and an LED indicates that the motor is working.
    Draw a circuit diagram of this. [Hint: you should use a relay]

13. (a) Draw a truth table for the system below.

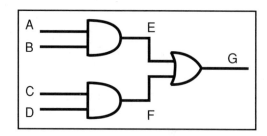

(b) If the inputs A,B,C & D represent push switches, which switches need to be pressed to obtain an output at G?

14. On a washing machine, the motor will not work until the door is closed, the on/off button is pressed and the water is at the right level.

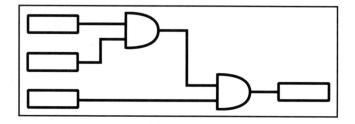

(i) Redraw the diagram above and label it.

(ii) Draw a truth table to show when the motor works.

THE EARTH AND ITS PLACE IN SPACE

The Universe

The Universe is so vast that we reach the limits of our minds in trying to understand it. In our crowded world, it is difficult to relate to the sheer quantity of emptiness which we call **SPACE.**

Distances, although they can be expressed mathematically, are so big that they do not relate to our own experiences.

However, thanks to an ever increasing knowledge of science and progress in the technology of astronomy, we are able to build up a picture of what the Universe is like, and where we are placed in it.

Within the Universe, there are over 100 Billion **Galaxies**. Modern techniques of observation, together with application of physics knowledge, lead scientists to believe that the galaxies are moving away from each other and that the Universe is **expanding**. This belief is part of the theory (the **Big Bang Theory**) which tries to explain how the Universe began.

So, What Is A Galaxy?

The name galaxy is given to a group of stars. A galaxy contains over 100 000 million stars.

Our galaxy is called the **MILKY WAY** and the band of stars which you can see with the naked eye in the night sky is really the edge of this galaxy.

Even so, although there are so many stars in a galaxy, there is no sense at all of crowding! In our galaxy the nearest star to the Earth is the Sun which is 1.5 $\times$ 10^5 km away. The nearest visible star to Earth, other than the Sun, (called **ALPHA CENTURA**) is 4×10^{13} km away and it takes light travelling at 3 $\times$ 10^5 km/s over four years to reach us.

Our galaxy, the **MILKY WAY**, is shaped rather like a spread out, and is so large that it takes light 100 000 years to cross it. Because the distance is so huge, it is not convenient to measure it in millions of km, so we use the term **LIGHT YEARS** to express astronomical distances. So we say that the distance across the Milky Way is 100 000 Light Years.

Fig 13.1 Milky Way as viewed from the side

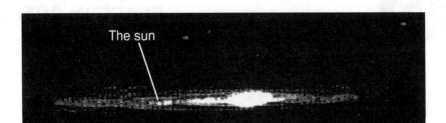

We now know that the Milky Way is but one of a cluster of about 30 galaxies in our 'area' of space and, in fact, is one of the two largest in the cluster. The other being the **ANDROMEDA** Galaxy, which is about 2 million Light Years away.

What Is A Light Year - And How Does It Relate To Distance?

A Light Year is the distance travelled by light in one year. It is important to remember that **nothing** can travel **faster** than light.

Light travels at a speed of 300 000 km/s (or 3×10^5 km/s).
There are about 30 000 000 or 3×10^7 seconds in one year.

$$
\begin{aligned}
\text{Distance travelled} \quad &= \text{Speed} \times \text{Time} \\
&= 3 \times 10^5 \text{ km/s} \times 3 \times 10^7 \text{ s} \\
&= 9 \times 10^{12} \text{ km}
\end{aligned}
$$

So the **distance** 9×10^{12} km, is known as one **LIGHT YEAR.**

To give you an idea of how large this is, it is about 600 000 times greater than the distance from the Earth to the Sun.

What Is A Star?

Stars are balls of gas which are extremely hot and glow brightly because of the nuclear reactions which are taking place deep within them. These reactions release an immense amount of energy. For example, the temperatures on the Sun range from 6 000 ˚C on the surface, to 15 000 000 ˚C in the centre.

Energy is radiated from them in the form of waves. The waves vary in length from the long Radio Waves (which is why a Radio Telescope is used to detect stars), through the Infra Red, Visible Light and Ultraviolet Waves, to the very short X-rays and Gamma rays.

Because Visible Light Waves are radiated from stars, we say that stars are **light sources** and so we can see them with the use of optical telescopes.

Planets can also be seen and, to the naked eye, look like points of light similar to stars. However, planets are not hot enough to give off their own light and we can see them **only** because light from the Sun is reflected off them.

The Sun, our nearest star, is our main source of energy and ,of the total radiation which we receive from the Sun, over 90% is in the form of Infra Red waves. Luckily for us our atmosphere, and especially the Ozone Layer, absorbs much of the Ultraviolet radiation. It is this particular form of radiation which gives us a suntan, although too much of it can sometimes lead to skin problems.

Fine - But Where, On Earth Are We?

Within our galaxy lies the Sun, orbited by the planets (including Earth), which go to make up our **SOLAR SYSTEM.**

You will see from Fig 13.2 that the Sun is located on one of the 'arms' of the Milky Way. The Sun is the centre of our **SOLAR SYSTEM** of which the Earth is a part.

Fig 13.2. Milky Way as viewed from the top

Sun

What Do You Know About The Universe?

1. What is a star?

2. What is a galaxy?

3. What is the name of the Earth's galaxy?

4. (a)What is the name of the other main galaxy in our cluster of galaxies?
    (b) How far is this galaxy from Earth in:
    (i) Light Years;   (ii) kilometres.

5. What is a Light Year?

6. Given that light travels at a speed of 3×10^5 km/s and that there are 3×10^7 seconds in a year, what is the distance (in km) of a Light Year? Show your working.

7. What do scientists believe about galaxies that enable them to say that the Universe is expanding?

8. A star, such as the Sun, radiates energy in the form of waves. Where does this energy come from?

Further Questions About The Universe

1. Planets and stars can be seen as points of light with the naked eye. Say how this is so, given that stars are entirely different from planets.

2. Describe two methods of observing stars and say why each method is possible.

Data for Questions 3, 4 and 5.
Light and Radio waves travel at 3×10^5 km/s.
There are approximately 3×10^7 seconds in a year.
The distance from the Earth to the nearest star (Alpha Centura) is 4×10^{13} km.

3. How long would it take a radio signal to be received on Earth after it had been sent to, and reflected from, the nearest star (Alpha Centura)? Use **seconds** as the unit for your answer.

4. Assuming you had a spacecraft which could travel at 15 km/s, how long would it take you to reach the nearest star (Alpha Centura):
    (i) in seconds: (ii) in years?

5. Will it ever be possible to have a manned space flight to Alpha Centura? Give a reason for your answer.

6. What does the Big Bang Theory try to explain and why is the idea of an expanding universe part of this theory?

THE EARTH AND ITS PLACE IN THE SOLAR SYSTEM

The nearest star to the Earth is the Sun. The Earth together with the other main planets, and their moons, orbit the Sun making what is known as the **SOLAR SYSTEM.**

Looking at figure 14.1, you will see that there are two groups of planets separated by the Asteroid Belt.

Fig 14.1

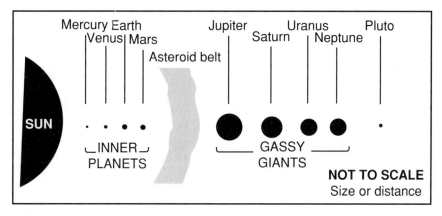

The Inner planets are sometimes called 'Rocky Dwarfs', whereas the outer planets are known as 'Gassy Giants'. These names give you clues to the main composition of the planets as well as their relative sizes.

Table 1

	Distance from Sun (Milion km)	Diameter (km)	Average Surface Temp ”C	Time for one orbit (year)
THE INNER PLANETS				
MERCURY	58	4 900	3 500	0.24
VENUS	108	12 100	480	0.6
EARTH	150	12 800	22	1.0
MARS	228	6 000	-23	1.9
THE GASSY GIANTS				
JUPITAR	778	143 000	-150	11.9
SATURN	427	120 000	-180	29.5
URANUS	2 870	51 000	-210	84.0
NEPTUNE	5 900	49 000	-220	164.9
PLUTO*	5 900	8 000	-230	247.0

Between the Inner and Outer planet is a group of bodies known as **ASTEROIDS**. There are thousands of these. They are rocky fragments which vary in size from a few metres to 1 000km in diameter forming what is known as the **Asteroid Belt**.

* Differs from the other 'Gassy Giants' in that it is of a higher density and is probably made of rock.

The Earth's Orbit

The Earth takes 365¼ days to go around the Sun in a path called an **orbit**. The length of time which it takes to complete one orbit is what we call a **year**. Once every four years we have to add an extra day to our calendar (February 29th) to accommodate the extra quarter day. Thus one in every four years is called a **Leap Year**.

The orbit is shaped like a 'squashed circle' and is called an **ellipse.**

As the Earth travels in space, it also spins on its own axis **once** every 24 hours which gives rise to **night** and **day.**

Daytime occurs in that part of the Earth *which is facing the Sun.* The other part of the Earth is in darkness, which we call night-time. During night-time, the only light which we receive is reflected light from the Moon and the faint amount of light emitted by distant stars.

Fig 14.2

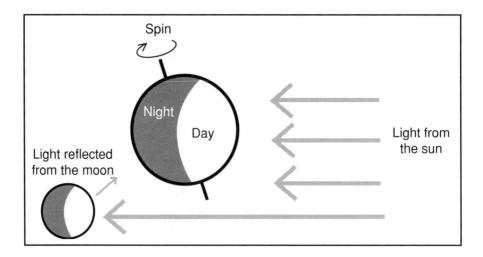

Why Is The Earth Hotter At The Equator Than At The Poles?

Fig 14.3

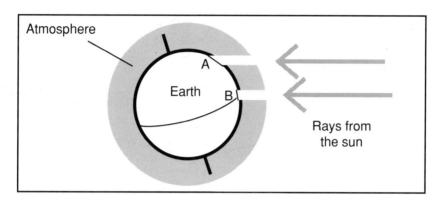

The diagram is self-explanatory, as it shows that the Sun's rays which fall on A have more of the atmosphere to pass through than rays which fall on B. Thus more of the energy will be absorbed by the atmosphere at A than at B, which in turn results in higher temperatures at B.

What Is A Moon?

A moon is really a body which orbits a planet. Such a body is given the general name **SATELLITE.** Each of the planets, except Mercury and Venus, have at least one such satellite.

Some planets have many such satellites (moons), e.g. Jupiter has 16, Saturn has 15.

The Earth has one, the **Moon**, which is about 380 000 km from Earth and has a diameter of about 5 000 km, a rocky surface and no atmosphere. It is thought that it was formed about 4 500 million years ago.

Because the Moon is not a light source, it is hard to see it during daytime. We see it best during night-time, because light from the Sun is reflected from it. We do not always see the same amount of Moon each night, because of the change in its orbit.

Fig 14.4 The Moon's Orbit About Earth

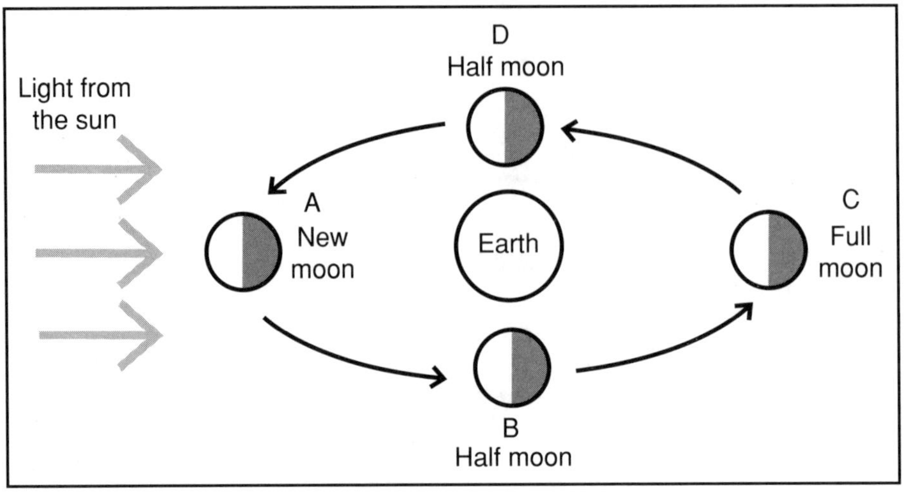

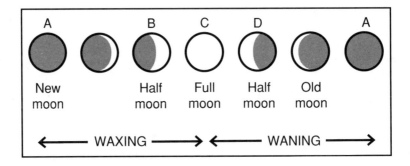

We call the changes in shape of the Moon, **PHASES**.

Fig 14.5. Phases of the Moon - as seen from Earth.

The Moon takes just under 28 days to complete one orbit of the Earth. Like the Earth, which spins round once on its axis every 24 hours, the Moon takes 27 days to spin round once. This is why we always have the same side of the Moon always pointing towards us on Earth.

Because there is no atmosphere, the temperature range of the Moon's surface is extreme and ranges from over 100 °C during the day, to less than −150 °C during the night.

Reasons For The Seasons

The Earth's axis is not vertical but is tilted by about 23^0. This means that at any one time, part of the Earth's surface is closer to the Sun than others.

Fig 14.6

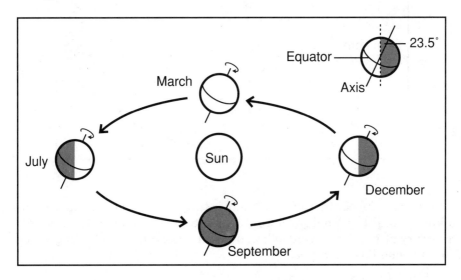

Fig 14.7

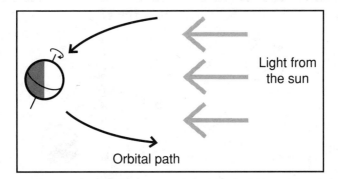

In July, the Northern Hemisphere is tilted **towards** the Sun resulting in **longer** days than nights, and higher temperatures i.e. Summer. The Sun is **high** in the sky at midday, following a path from Rising to Setting which is **South** of due East and West.

Fig 14.8

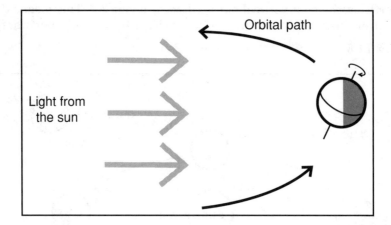

In December, the Northern Hemisphere is tilted **away** from the Sun resulting in **longer nights** than days, lower temperatures i.e. Winter. The Sun is **low** in the sky at midday having followed a path from Rising to Setting which is **North** of due East and West.

Fig 14.9 The Equinoxes

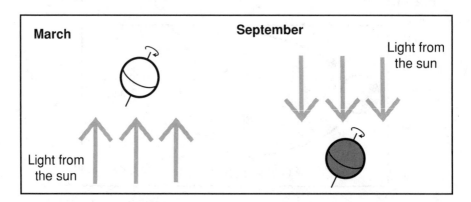

There are two days in the year (21st March, 21st September) called the EQUINOXES, when the length of the day and night are **equal**. On these two days, the Sun's path follows **exactly** a path from East to West.

What Do You Know About The Earth And Solar System?

1. Why do we experience night and day?

2. (i) How long does it take for the Earth to complete one orbit of the Sun?
   (ii) What do we call this period of time?

3. Why do we have seasons on Earth?

4. Draw a diagram to show how the four seasons occur.

5. Explain, using a diagram, why, in the Northern Hemisphere, Summer days are longer than Summer nights.

6. Draw a horizon. Imagine that you are in England facing due South. Draw a labelled diagram to show the path of the Sun from rise through midday to sunset for the following dates:
   (i) 21st December, (ii) 21st March, (iii) 21st June.
   There will be three paths on your diagram, so be sure to label each one carefully.

7. Name the planets in our Solar System which are smaller than the Earth.

8. Name the (i) smallest, (ii) largest planet in our Solar System.

9. '..till the Moon shall wax and wane no more.' Explain what is meant by the terms, 'wax' and 'wane'.

10. Draw a diagram to show how the Moon looks when viewed from Earth during the following phases:
    (i)   Waxing crescent;
    (ii) Full moon;
    (iii) Last quarter.

Further Questions On The Earth And Solar System

1. Look at Table 1.
    (i) What is the closest possible distance between Earth and Mars?
    (ii) What is the furthest separation that can take place between Earth and Jupiter?
    (iii) The atmosphere on Venus is said to contain Carbon Dioxide. What piece of information given in the table would help to confirm this? Give a reason for your answer.

2. If you could observe from the Sun, which would *look* bigger, Mercury or Venus? Give a reason for your answer.

3. Assume the following:
    The Earth's orbit is circular; take $\pi = 3$; number of seconds in a year 3×10^7.
    (i) How far does the Earth travel in its orbit in one Year?
    (ii) What is its average speed in km/s?

4. (i) Using Table 1, plot a graph to show how the distances from the Sun ($\underline{x}$ axis) is related, if at all, to the surface temperatures of the Inner planets.
    (ii) Comment on your results.

5. Assume that an asteroid is 500 million km from the Sun.
    Give reasonable value, saying what assumptions you have made, for:
    (i) its average temperature;
    (ii) the length (in days) of one of its 'years'.

MAN EXPLORES THE SOLAR SYSTEM

"The cow jumped over the moon", Startrek, Starwars are mere examples of man's fascination with space exploration. However, the enormous bullet capsule which Jules Verne described being fired from a huge gun, did not, in the end, turn out to be the method used to enable man to travel to the Moon.

It was during the Second World War (1939-1945) that the technology to fire a rocket at an enemy much further away than the largest gun could shoot, came to fruition. The V1 and V2 rockets, developed by the Germans, caused much damage and distress. These rockets were launched from the European mainland and were designed so that the motor would stop when the rocket, full of explosive, was over the specified target. The rocket fell to the ground causing extensive damage. Many places in the South Eastern part of England were badly hit by these weapons, with London and its docklands situated in its East End having a particularly bad time.

However, after the war, this technology was used as a starting point for man's exploration of space.

We have already seen that the Moon is a satellite because it orbits the Earth.

In 1957, the USSR launched the first man-made satellite to orbit the Earth. It was called **'SPUTNIK I'** and was unmanned. It carried a radio transmitter sending out regular 'bleeps' so that its path could be followed from the ground - with receivers which are the forerunners of the dishes used to receive 'Satellite Television' today.

In 1959, the Russians launched the first of two spacecraft whose purpose was to study the Moon. The first , **LUNIK II**, actually hit the Moon and made a crash landing. The second, **LUNIK III,** was able to take pictures of the far side of the Moon. You will remember that this had never been seen before because the Moon only spins round once every 27 days and thus shows the same side to the Earth all the time.

In 1961, the USSR launched **VOSTOK I** which took the first man, Yuri Gagarin, into space. He completed one orbit of the Earth before being brought back to a hero's welcome.

One year later, the USA launched **FRIENDSHIP VII** which contained John Glenn, the first American in space. He completed three orbits of the Earth before being brought safely back.

Clearly, the possibility of manned spaceflights which had been dreamed of for so long, were on the verge of being fulfilled and the famous 'Race' between the USSR and the USA to put a man on the Moon was now really on and hotting up.

By 1966, the USSR seemed to be winning as they launched the **LUNAR IX**, which was able to land an unmanned spacecraft on the Moon - this time without crashing.

However, in 1969, the USA launched the now famous **APOLLO XI**, which successfully landed two Americans, Neil Armstrong and Edwin 'Buzz' Aldrin, on the Moon in a Lunar module called 'Eagle'.

This is such an important step in the history of space exploration, that it is worth looking at this mission in some detail.

1st Phase - Launch

The Apollo spacecraft was on top of a SATURN 5 launch vehicle. This was an immense rocket which was really three separate rockets in one. The first and biggest part was able to lift the Saturn 5 to a height of 64km. When this height was reached, the first stage fell away and the second stage rockets then burned for 6½ minutes to propel the spacecraft more than 160km above the Earth and a further 1600km away from the launch pad. When this had been completed, the second stage fell away leaving the third stage rocket to put Apollo XI into orbit around the Earth.

Fig 15.1 Schematic of the Moon Rocket

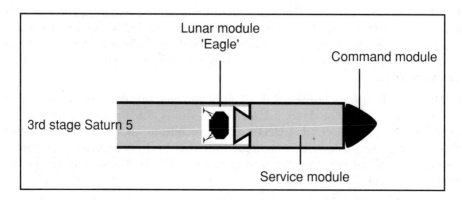

After 1½ orbits of the Earth, the third stage then burns again to propel the Apollo towards the Moon.

2nd Phase - The Flight To The Moon

During the spaceflight, the Apollo XI crew separated the SERVICE and COMMAND MODULES from the third stage, turned these modules round and 'docked' with the LUNAR module.

Fig 15.2

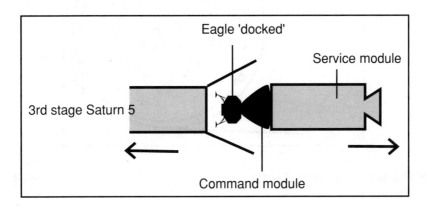

When the turning and docking had been completed, the third stage of the Saturn 5 rocket fell away.

As the Apollo XI flew to the Moon, the craft rotated slowly so that the Sun's rays heated it evenly, otherwise one side of the craft would have become unbearably hot. This phase of the journey lasted for 73 hours.

3rd Phase - Orbit And Landing.

(a) The Command Module engine burned to slow the craft so that it went into orbit around the Moon.

(b) Two astronauts, Armstrong and Aldrin in the Lunar Module (**Eagle**), separated from the command module (**Columbia**), containing the third astronaut, Collins, leaving it in Lunar orbit.

(c) Going behind the Moon, the Eagle fired the descent engine and landed- with only 20 seconds of fuel remaining.

(d) After 22 hours on the Moon, Eagle lifted off to rejoin Columbia.

(e) Eagle joined the Command Module and the crew members were reunited and safe within Columbia. The Lunar Module was separated and Eagle was left behind in Lunar orbit as the Command Module headed for home.

Fig 15.3

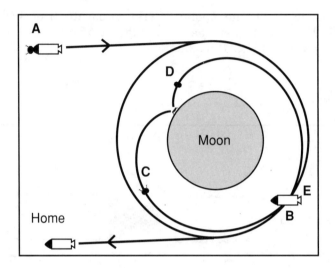

4th Phase - Return Home

Just before re-entering the Earth's atmosphere, the Service Module was separated from the Command Module. The Command Module turned round so that its blunt side, containing a heat shield, faced the Earth.

8 days after the initial launch, the Command Module splashed down safely in the South Pacific and the astronauts were picked up by the US Navy. In order to ensure that the Earth was guarded against possible contamination, the astronauts spent the next 17 days in quarantine.

The final Apollo mission to the Moon was in 1972. Here, the Apollo XVIII astronauts spent three days on the Moon and carried out many experiments, as well as bringing back samples of sand and rock. Because there is no oxygen or water on the Moon, the surface rock is well preserved and has been useful in helping us to study what the Earth was like millions of years ago. The samples brought back showed that the rocks were volcanic and similar to the Basalt rocks found on Earth.

MISSIONS TO OTHER PLANETS

1965 saw the start of the **MARINER** series of missions to explore the planet **MARS**. These were purely close observational missions and no attempt was made to land on the planet until the **VIKING** missions in 1976. The Viking missions involved sending up a robotically controlled landing module, thus using the technology gained from the 1969 Lunar Apollo missions. The object of these missions was to retrieve as much data as possible, including samples of rock, from the surface of Mars.

In 1973, **PIONEER 10** sent back the first pictures of Jupiter and it was hoped that the spacecraft would travel to the outer planets and bring back pictures of Neptune, but it did not get close enough to the planet to do so.

By far the most spectacular of the missions to explore the outer planets so far, have been the **VOYAGER 1** and **VOYAGER 2** missions launched in 1977.

In 1979 Voyager 1 went very close to Jupiter and brought back the clearest yet pictures of this planet and its moons. In fact, on one of its moons, Io, pictures were sent back of the first volcanic eruption ever recorded on a planet other than the Earth.

Voyager 2 also went by Jupiter and then on to the outer planets including Saturn (1981), Uranus (1986) and Neptune(1989). After Neptune the Voyager went out of our Solar System and is now somewhere in deepest space.

Benefits Of The Space Programme

Although the cost of space exploration is very high, the research, carried out by the National Aeronautics and Space Administration (NASA), has led to practical ideas which are now used in our daily lives. Some examples are given below.

Benefits To Medical Science:

1) Lens Coating: Developed to protect plastic surfaces on space equipment, it hardens the lens and increases its resistance to scratches. This is one of the most widely used spin-offs and is used on many forms of eye-wear such as glasses and goggles.
2) Advanced Pacemaker: Using technology that controls communications between satellites and the Earth, pacemakers which have been implanted and which can mimic rhythms of the heart, can be controlled from outside the body.

Benefits To Home And Industry

3) Water purification: The technology which was developed to purify water on board space shuttles, is now used to purify and soften water in home and industrial systems.

4) Cordless products: Needing cordless tools to collect samples on the Moon, Black & Decker developed the technology which is now widely used in many consumer products.

5) Cool Suit: Originally used to cool astronauts in space, it is now used to help protect fire-fighters, surgeons and motor racing drivers.

Benefits To Communications:

6) Satellite Technology: There are now hundreds of satellites which orbit the Earth. Some of these are to observe the Earth from a distance, thereby giving us information about the natural conditions e.g. weather, monitoring of the composition of the atmosphere and condition of the rain forests. Some have military uses and are used to 'observe goings on' in other nations. Some carry telescopes (e.g. the Hubble Telescope) which point out towards space and provide a clearer view of the stars than the telescopes on Earth where the light from stars has to pass through our atmosphere before it reaches the observer.

Some satellites, particularly those used for communication purposes, are put into an orbit where they travel round at the same speed as the rotation of the Earth. These satellites are called **GEOSTATIONARY** satellites, because they are always above the **same spot** on the Earth.

Fig 15.4 A Geostationary Satellite

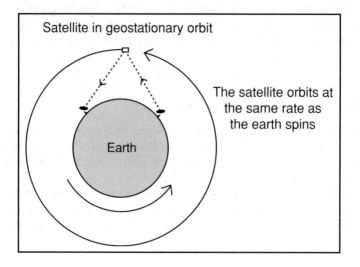

What Do You Know About Man's Exploration Of Space?

1. Say which part of our Solar System was each of the following missions hoping to explore:
   (a) MARINER,   (b) VOYAGER,   (c) LUNIK,
   (d) PIONEER,   (e) APOLLO.

2. What was/is EAGLE and where is it now?

3. The HUBBLE telescope operates from a satellite. Why should this provide better pictures of space than land-based telescopes?

4. Explain a GEOSTATIONARY SATELLITE.

5. What was SPUTNIK and what did it do?

6. SATURN V is a 'three stage' rocket. What does 'three stage' mean and why is this particular aspect of the design needed?

7. VOYAGER I sent back some really good pictures of Jupiter and its moons. What was particularly exciting about the pictures of the moon Io?

8. What useful observations about the Earth do you think that an orbiting satellite could make? (Exclude military objectives in your answer.)

9. Give **three** examples where research for space exploration has provided everyday benefits to life on Earth.

WHAT IS THE EARTH MADE OF?

A Difficulty

Fig 16.1

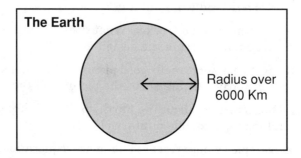

"If I dug a hole from England to Australia....." is a popular idea which is often expressed. If that were possible, you would be able to analyse the rocks lining your hole as you dug it.

However, man's deepest drill and boreholes reach only but a few kilometres and certainly do not even puncture the Earth's crust. Even volcanoes, which erupt molten rock originated some 80 - 100km below the surface, only give us part of the story. The fact that the rock is molten as it erupts, gives us the clue that digging such a hole would not be possible.

So how are we going to find out what the interior of the Earth is like?

Some Clues Using Our Knowledge Of Physics

1. Using Density

The average density of the Earth is about 5.5 g/cm³ but yet the densities of rocks from the Crust are generally within the range 2.5 - 3.5 g/cm³.

This **must** mean that the **interior** contains material which has a **greater** density than the rocks at the Earth's surface.

Using Gravity

Sir Isaac Newton knew that the Earth was slightly 'flattened' because of the difference in Gravitational Force between the Equator and the North Pole.

He knew that gravity exerted **less** force at the **Equator** than it did at the North Pole.

If you took two objects of exactly the same **MASS**, the object at the Equator would **WEIGH** slightly **less** than the object at the North Pole.

As, **weight = mass × gravitational force**

and **mass remains the same** -wherever you are

then clearly, if the **weight** is slightly less at the Equator and the **mass** remains the same, the gravitational force is slightly less at the Equator than it is at the North Pole.

Now, as G/F is inversely proportional to the distance between the centres of the masses (which means that the force **decreases** as the masses become **further** apart), then an object on the Earth's surface at the Equator must be slightly further away from the Earth's centre than the same object on the Earth's surface at the North Pole.

Fig 16.2

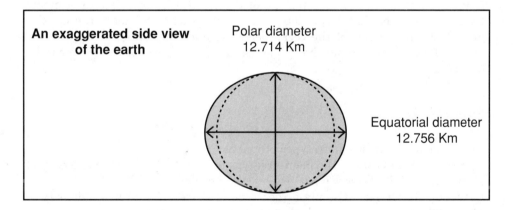

An exaggerated side view of the earth
Polar diameter
12.714 Km

Equatorial diameter
12.756 Km

This slight flattening is caused by the rotation of the Earth and shows that there is material in the interior which can change shape (just as liquids do). We already know from volcanic activity that there are rocks in molten form beneath the crust.

Is The Interior Completely Liquid?

When an earthquake takes place, vast amounts of energy are released and some of this energy is sent through the rocks of the Earth's interior in the form of shock waves. Clearly, much of the energy is used to destroy cities and buildings located in the path of the shocks.

By studying the shock waves produced by earthquakes (and man-made underground explosions), it is possible to build up a picture of the various types of rocks forming the interior of the Earth - and the States (i.e. solid or liquid) of them.

The study of earthquakes is called **SEISMOLOGY** and the instrument which is used to measure the shock waves is called a **SEISMOMETER.** This is a very sensitive instrument and is able to detect vibrations of the Earth that may only be 10^{-6}m (0.000 001m) in size.

There are various types of shock wave from earthquakes and their paths are different depending on their type. Some pass through the centre of the Earth and it is by gathering evidence from all of these which enables us to build up a picture of what the interior of the Earth is like - even though we cannot dig our famous hole through it.

Possible Structure Of The Earth

It must be stressed that our picture of the Earth's interior is only a model based on the seismic information which enables us to calculate the density and elastic properties of the rocks below us and the depths of the various layers of rocks. No samples have been obtained and are not likely ever to be collected.

The Crust

This is made up of two main types of rock:
(i) Continental Crust - The main rock type being **GRANITE**, with a density of about 2.7g/cm³. The layer depth of this ranges from about 25 - 90km.
(ii) Oceanic Crust - The main rock type is **BASALT** and has a density of about 3.3 g/cm³. This is much thinner than continental crust and the layer depth of this ranges from 8 - 11km.

Fig. 16.3

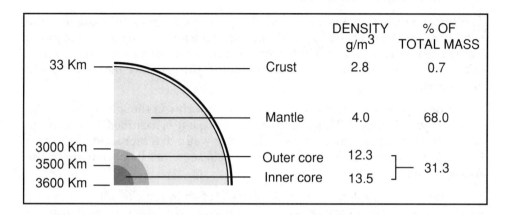

		DENSITY g/m^3	% OF TOTAL MASS
33 Km	Crust	2.8	0.7
	Mantle	4.0	68.0
3000 Km	Outer core	12.3	
3500 Km			31.3
3600 Km	Inner core	13.5	

The Mantle

This is mostly formed of solid rock which has an average density of about 4 g/cm^3. Thus the less dense Crust 'floats' on this. The main type of rock is called **PERIDOTITE** and it consists mainly of the two elements Silicon and Oxygen.

The mantle goes down to a depth of 2900 km and accounts for 68% of the Earth's mass.

The physical processes which take place within the mantle are too complex to detail here. However, it is sufficient, at this stage, to note that although most of the mantle is in a solid state, there are areas where the rock becomes liquid. It is this which allows a circulation between the innermost and outermost rocks.

The term for mantle rock in the molten state is **MAGMA**, and this can be brought to the Earth's surface and erupted as **LAVA**.

The Core

Here again, we are relying on the information about earthquake waves to indicate that below the mantle lies the core of the Earth.

The fact that some types of shock wave will **not** pass through the core, tells us that the outer part of the core is liquid. However, some types of shock wave **do** pass through the core, so we are able to say that the core is in two parts;

A liquid outer core surrounding the solid inner core.

The whole core accounts for about 31% of the total mass of the Earth, so we are looking at much denser materials.

The **outer core** is thought to be made up of molten iron sulphide and the density ranges from about 10 g/cm^3 just under the mantle, to about 12.3 g/cm^3. The density increases with depth because of the enormous compression which takes place (you will remember that in liquids, the pressure increases as you go deeper).

The **inner core** has a density of 13.5 g/cm^3 and this is thought to be a solid alloy of iron and nickel. This is not a wild guess, but is assumed, based on the composition of certain meteorites which may well have represented the core from other planets which have broken up. These meteorites originate in the Asteroid Belt.

The other piece of evidence is that the density of an iron/nickel alloy - allowing for the increase due to compression - is a good proximation to the density of 13.5 g/cm^3 which has been calculated as the density of the solid core, based on the information from earthquake waves.

What Do You Know About What The Earth Is Made Of?

1. Starting from the surface, put the layers listed below in the order in which you come across them as you travel to the Earth's centre:
   Outer core, mantle, crust, inner core.

2. What is the study of earthquakes called?

3. What instrument is used to measure shock waves in the Earth?

4. Why is our study of earthquake shockwaves so important to our study of the composition of the Earth?

5. What is transmitted by the waves produced by an earthquake?

6. Looking at the crust, name the main types of rock which go to make up (i) Continental Crust, (ii) Oceanic Crust.

7. What is the general name given to molten mantle rock?

8. What is the name given to molten rock which erupts at the Earth's surface?

9. How do we know that part of the Earth's core is liquid?

10. Name the main metal which is present in both the inner and outer core.

11. Name the main non-metal which is thought to be present in the outer core.

12. (i) If the core is just under J of the total mass of the Earth and has a mass of 2×10^{24} kg, what is the mass of the Earth?
    (ii) Assuming that the mass of the Crust is 1% of the Earth's total mass, calculate the mass (in kg) of the Crust.
    (iii) Use information from parts (i) and (ii) of this question to estimate the mass of the Mantle.

EARTHQUAKES AND VOLCANOES

We saw in Chapter 16, that shock waves produced by earthquakes are used to try and find out what the Earth's interior is like. Now we shall consider earthquakes in more detail.

Earthquakes occur because of movements along large cracks in the crust known as **FAULTS.**

Fig 17.1

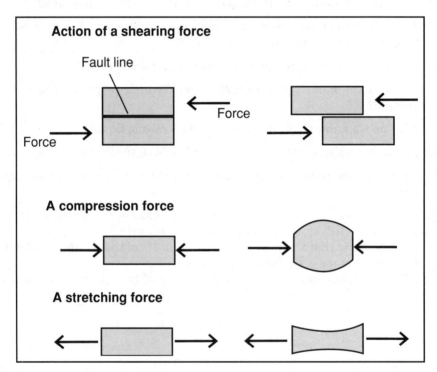

Movement is not continuous, but huge forces cause the rocks to be strained. This strain increases until there is a moment when the rocks break, causing a sudden movement which results in shock waves radiating out in various directions.

The type of force which causes this movement is called a **SHEARING FORCE.** This is so called because the forces acting on the rocks have a shearing effect, i.e. the rocks move past each other along the fault line.

Earthquake Epicentre And Focus

The spot where earthquake waves are generated is called the **EARTHQUAKE FOCUS**.

A Focus may be many kilometres deep underground, so a line is drawn from the Earth's centre to the surface passing through the focus. Where the line cuts the Earth's surface, is called the **EARTHQUAKE EPICENTRE**.

Fig 17.2

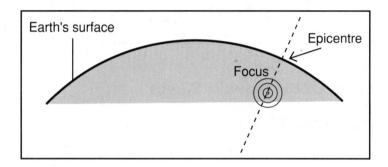

The **MAGNITUDE** of an earthquake registers the total energy released by the earthquake at the focus.

This is measured on the **RICHTER SCALE** which ranges from 1 – 9. Most earthquakes are between 3 and 8 in magnitude.

The **INTENSITY** of an earthquake describes the amount of damage which is done to the Earth's surface. This is measured on the **MERCALLI SCALE** which ranges from 12 *'catastrophic'* to 1 *'detected by instruments only'*.

How Do We Measure The Intensity Of Earthquake Waves?

As we saw in Chapter 16, we use an instrument called a **SEISMOMETER**. These are set to record waves in both horizontal and vertical directions. You will remember that an earthquake produces various types of waves and these will travel along different planes (i.e. horizontal or vertical) depending on the type of wave.

In principle, a seismometer consists of a heavy mass which remains stationary while the rest of the meter, which is in direct contact with the Earth, moves as the ground vibrates. The motions are recorded on a rotating drum and the resulting chart is called a **SEISMOGRAPH**.

Fig. 17.3

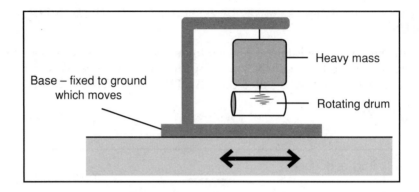

Main Types Of Earthquake Waves

(a) Compression Waves

If you take a 'Slinky' lay it on a bench with one end fixed and move the other end backwards and forwards **along the line** of the 'Slinky', then compression waves will be produced.

These waves will travel through solids **and** liquids and the speed of the waves will vary according to the density of the rocks through which they pass.

As a rule, waves will travel **faster** in **higher density** materials.

Fig 17.4

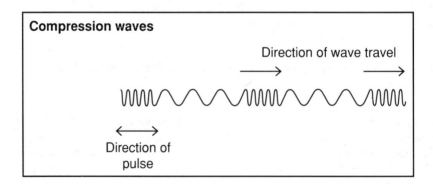

(b) Transverse Waves

With the 'Slinky' still fixed at one end, move the other end **from side to side**. This will result in the formation **(PROPAGATION)** of Transverse Waves.

In general, in the case of earthquakes, these waves are **slower** than compression waves and **cannot** travel through liquids.

Fig 17.5

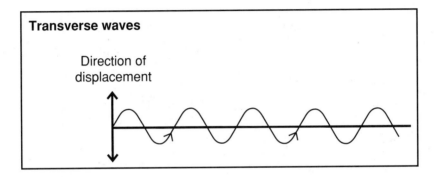

Because these two types of wave travel at different speeds, then they will arrive at the recording station at different times. This is a help in building up a picture of where the waves originated from in the first place and will also give information about the densities, and hence types, of rocks through which the waves have travelled.

As an earthquake will produce at least these two types of waves, it is the 'disappearance' of the transverse waves which allows us to realise that part of the Earth's interior is liquid.

Where Do Earthquakes Take Place?

The majority of earthquakes occur in relatively clearly defined SEISMIC ZONES. These tend to occur (a) where there are faults in the Earth's crust or (b) at the boundaries of crustal Plates. In both cases, giant forces build up such a strain in the rock, that movement occurs.

Fig 17.6

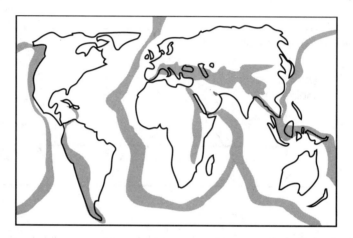

Volcanoes

Volcanoes are the holes **(VENTS)** in the Earth's crust through which molten magma from the mantle rises to the surface and erupts as **LAVA**.

As we saw earlier, when discussing what the interior of the Earth is like, the volcanic activity on the surface is evidence of a hot interior which is on the move.

Where Does The Energy Come From To Keep The Interior Hot?

There are two possibilities:

(i) The Earth could well retain part of its original thermal energy that it had when it was formed over 4 000 million years ago. Rocks are very poor conductors of thermal energy and so would form an insulating layer around the hot core thus preventing this energy from radiating away into space.

(ii) Thermal energy is released by the 'breaking up' **(DECAY)** of certain forms (called **RADIOACTIVE ISOTOPES**) of naturally occurring elements such as Uranium and Potassium. Although the composition of the Peridotite in the mantle would show that there are minute traces, in terms of 'parts per million', of the radioactive isotopes, it must be remembered that the mantle makes up 68% of the total mass of the Earth.

It is thought that there is enough of the mantle rock ,which contains radioactive isotopes, to enable it to release the necessary thermal energy to keep it at a high temperature - and thus some of it in the molten state.

Types of Volcanic Activity (Volcanism)

(i) Effusive Volcanism

Basalt Magma erupts as a free-flowing (LOW VISCOSITY) liquid at around 1100°C. The eruption will begin with an escape of gases which spray liquid basalt into the air. Liquid basalt then flows freely and spreads widely from around the vent and this can give rise to flattish, broad volcanoes with gently sloping sides. Some of the best examples of these are found in the Hawaiian Islands where some of these islands have built up as undersea mountains.

(ii) Explosive Volcanism

These occur when the lava is thicker and so there is a greater buildup of gas before there is a series of explosions which throw ash and pieces of rock, of all sizes, out. Sometimes, parts of the volcanic cone itself may be blown away. It was this type of volcanic eruption which destroyed the city of Pompeii in AD 79, Krakatoa in 1883 and 30 000 people on the island of Martinique when Mount Pelee erupted in 1902.

Where Will You Find A Volcano?

Clearly, where there is intense activity in the Earth's crust and in particular, in those regions where earthquakes are detected. The type of volcanic activity will depend upon the depth of the earthquake activity.

As a very general rule, earthquakes which are **near the surface** are associated with **Effusive Volcanism,**

whereas

Explosive Volcanic activity tends to occur in those areas where the earthquake activity is much deeper beneath the Earth's surface.

Other factors which need to be taken into consideration are geographical features of the crust (ocean, continent, mountain) and the crustal Plates which make up the Earth's surface.

Features Of Lava

You will know that if you try to make crystals quickly, then you will end up with tiny ones. Whereas, if you are careful and patient you will find that larger crystals are grown over a much longer time period.

So it is with rocks. Those rocks which cool slowly will form much larger crystals of the compounds within them than those which cool quickly.

Erupting lava will cool and solidify very quickly and any crystals which are formed will be very small.

This means that erupting lava will crystallise at the Earth's surface and thus produce rocks which are very fine grained (i.e. they will contain very small crystals).

What Do You Know About Earthquakes?

1. What is the name given to a crack in the Earth's crust?

2. Draw labelled diagrams to show that you understand the action of:
    (i) a shearing force (ii) a compression force (iii) a stretching force.

3. Explain where the following are located:
    (i) an earthquake focus,   (ii) an earthquake epicentre.

4. Name two types of shockwave produced by an earthquake.

5. Which type of waves will not go through liquids?

6. (a) What is the name and range of the scale used to measure the intensity of an earthquake?
    (b) What does the INTENSITY of an earthquake describe?

7. Say, giving a reason, which of the following types of shockwave will be recorded first on a seismograph: a transverse wave or a compression wave?

What Do You Know About Volcanoes?

1. Complete the following sentences:
    (a) Molten rock within the .... is called ....
    (b) When........................ is erupted from a volcano it is called..............
    (c) The hole in a volcano through which .... erupts is called the
    ....

2. What type of volcanic activity is associated with shallow earthquakes?

3. Describe, giving a reason, a feature which is common to all types of lava.

4. Give two possible explanations as to why the mantle is hot enough to keep some of the Peridotite molten.

5. Explain - giving examples - as many differences as you can, between an effusive and an explosive volcano.

THE EARTH'S EVER CHANGING SURFACE

An Introduction To Plate Tectonics

From the evidence gained from meteorites, it is thought that the Moon, as well as the Earth and other planets in our Solar System, was formed about 4 600 million years ago. Analysis of the rock samples brought back by the Apollo astronauts shows that the surface of the Moon is about 3 000 million years old.

The craters which will have been formed early in the Moon's history and were produced by meteor bombardment and volcanic activity, have been well preserved and can be seen clearly.

This is evidence of a lack of surface erosion, or any recent crustal activity, and is in contrast with the situation here on Earth.

On Earth, a meteor crater is a very rare find - even though it is reasonable to assume that the Earth suffered the same meteor bombardment that the Moon experienced early in its history.

The majority of the Earth's craters have 'disappeared' with the passage of time and this is clear evidence that erosion has taken place and that the Earth's crust is 'active' and ever-changing.

Another pointer is that there is a wide range in the ages and types of rocks found on the Earth's surface.

The earliest rocks are some 3 800 million years old and occur in areas where there is virtually no volcanic or earthquake activity. These rocks tend to be found in flat, gently undulating areas with rounded-topped hills - the sort of terrain which is common to the central plains of North America and Canada.

The youngest rocks, formed from 60 million years ago to the present, are found in areas where there is a great deal of volcanic and earthquake activity. These rocks tend to be found in dramatic regions containing rugged mountain ranges with 'sharp' mountain tops, as shown by the mountain ranges of the Andes, Alps and Himalayas.

The processes of erosion leading to the disappearance of the meteor craters, also caused the Continental Crust to be broken up and deposited in the oceans. If this were a 'One-way' process and the material was not replaced, then the whole land mass would have disappeared under an ocean covering the entire surface of the Earth.

The fact that this has not happened and that the amount of Continental Crust is increasing, tells us that the Continental Crust is being replaced at a greater rate than it is being eroded. We know that volcanoes are found where there is earthquake activity and that earthquakes are caused by movements in the Earth's Crust.

Other Evidence Of Activity In The Earth's Crust

If we look at the fossilised remains of organisms, we can tell that Britain was once in a tropical region of the Earth. It is also possible, again by looking at the fossil record and rock types, that South America and Africa were part of the same land mass, some 150 million years ago. So, incredible as it may sound, there is evidence that the Continents have been, and are, moving. This certainly indicates major activity in the Earth's Crust and we shall now look at this in more detail.

The Crustal Plate Theory

Observations and careful measurements suggest that the Earth's surface is composed of between 10 and 20 plates which are made of Crust and upper layers of Mantle - and that these plates are, to a greater or lesser extent, moving. The edges of the plates are called MARGINS and we shall look at the two main types of margin.

1. Constructive Margins

These are where the plates are '**made**'. They are found in the ocean ridges of which the Mid - Atlantic Ridge is an example. This is an undersea 'mountain' range running from the east of Greenland down through the centre of the Atlantic ocean to the Antarctic.

Fig 18.1

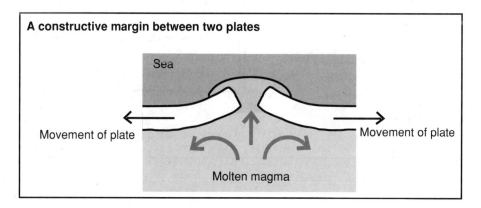

A constructive margin between two plates

Sea

Movement of plate

Movement of plate

Molten magma

Ocean ridges are formed by molten mantle rising between the two oceanic plates and hardening, causing the plates to be pushed apart.

These ocean ridges form the world's largest mountain chain with a total length of more than 50 000km. The ridges have an average width of about 1 000km and they can rise to around 5km above the surrounding seabed. Along these ridges will be the effusive volcanic type of activity with a steady outpouring of lava. It is thought that there are convection currents in the mantle, where hot magma rises and circulates (rather like hot water rising and cold water sinking to take its place in a domestic boiler) and that mid-ocean ridges occur above points of upward convection of molten magma.

2. Destructive Plate Margins

These margins are where plates are 'destroyed'. They sink beneath the adjoining plate and the oceanic crustal material is melted in the mantle. When there is a destructive plate margin between two oceanic plates or an oceanic plate with a continental plate, then deep ocean trenches are formed.

The earthquake activity originates along the slope of the plate margins (see 'X X X' on fig 18.2) and you will see that the foci of the earthquakes will vary from shallow to deep under the surface.

Along the length of a destructive plate margin, there is the strong possibility of explosive volcanic activity. It is along these margins that the world's great mountain ranges (e.g. Rockies, Andes) have been formed.

Fig. 18.2

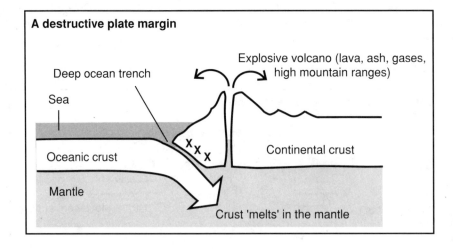

The Himalayas are also located at a destructive plate margin, but this time the boundary is between two continental plates. So, although there is the possibility of some shallow earthquake activity, there is usually no volcanic activity associated with these plate margins.

Plate Tectonics

The study of the crustal plates and their movement is called PLATE TECTONICS. This is a relatively new branch of scientific study and, in fact, many of the major ideas which we accept today were only formulated as little as 30 years ago.

There are still questions to be answered and not all of the plate margins are known to this day. The exact mechanism of how plates are made is still a matter for conjecture, as the real answer lies deep in the inaccessible mantle!

What Do You Know About Plate Tectonics?

1. What is a plate thought to consist of?

2. Roughly (to the nearest 5) how many plates cover the Earth's surface?

3. What is a 'plate margin'?

4. What happens to a plate at a constructive margin?

5. What happens to a plate at a destructive margin?

6. Say what type of plate margin is found near each of the following features:
    i)   deep ocean trenches;
    ii) ocean ridges;
    iii) explosive volcanic activity;
    iv) high mountain ranges;
    v)   upward convection currents in the mantle;
    vi) effusive volcanic activity.

More Questions On Plate Tectonics

1. List the main pieces of evidence which tell us that:
   i)   there is crustal activity on the Earth;
   ii) that the continents are continually being added to;
   iii) that the continents are moving.

2. Assuming that the South Atlantic ocean is 5 000 km wide at the Equator and that the break up between Africa and South America started 125 million years ago, what would be the rate of 'opening' between these two continents? (hint: work in cm)

3. Use the following information to answer this question.
   Approximate age of the Earth; 4 600 million years.
   71% of the Earth is covered by water.
   60% of the Earth's crust is Oceanic crust - density range: 2.8 - 2.9 g/cm³.
   40% of the Earth's crust is Continental crust - density range 2.6 - 2.8 g/cm³
   The volume of the land mass is 1.3×10^8 km³.
   The volume of land mass eroded each year is 13 km³.
   (i) Why does oceanic crust nearly always sink under continental crust at a destructive plate margin?
   ii) Will the seabed be always Oceanic Crust?
   iii) Assuming no replacement, how long would it take for all of the land mass to be eroded into the sea?

4. Describe the evidence for assuming that Oceanic Crust is 'made' at ocean ridges.

5. Account, as fully as you can, for the differences between the landforms that are found in the Canadian Prairies and the Rocky Mountains.

ROCKS OF THE EARTH

The study of rocks and minerals is known as **GEOLOGY** and your experience will tell you that there is a great variety of many types of rock. Before looking at the different types of rock, it is worth considering what a rock is.

What Is A Rock?

Rock is simply a mass of grains of minerals which have been cemented together, or the grains have crystallised into a single mass.

What Is A Mineral?

It is a naturally occurring element or compound which possesses a definite crystal structure. A good example of a mineral is diamond, which is a crystalline version of the element carbon.

More About Minerals

About 75% of the Earth's Crust is made up of the two elements Silicon (28%) and Oxygen (47%). These two elements combine to form SILICATES.

Sand

Sand (or Silica) is an oxide of silicon and is a mineral which is probably very familiar to you. Not only is it found on beaches and deserts, but it has a wide variety of uses. It is the raw material for making glass. You may have noticed that test tubes are made from different types of glass.

Some test tubes will be easy to break and do not stand much heating. These are made from glass which is made by heating

limestone, sodium carbonate and sand - sometimes called **Soda Glass**.

The hard-glass test tubes will be made from sand and boron oxide (**Borosilicate glass, 'Pyrex'**) and this enables them to withstand much greater temperatures.

Your parents may well have some fine 'cut-crystal' glass at home - this will be used for wine glasses, decanters and bowls and other ornamental objects. This form of glass is made from sand which has been heated with lead oxide and this combination makes the glass 'sparkle' - particularly at the places where the glass is cut.

Sand is a hard mineral and small grains of it are glued onto paper to make **'Sandpaper'**. You will have used this in the workshop.

An important use of sand is in the building industry, where it is mixed with cement to make **MORTAR**, a material used to bind the bricks together.

If you add small stones to a mortar mix, you will end up with **CONCRETE.**

The increasing use of concrete is mainly responsible for the development in buildings and large construction projects (e.g. skyscrapers, dams, bridges, motorways) which is constantly taking place.

For larger projects **REINFORCED CONCRETE** is used. This is concrete which has a network of iron rods running through it and which adds to the overall strength of the concrete. Concrete is at its strongest when being compressed - hence it is used for the foundations of buildings.

However, it is not as strong when it is being pushed sideways (see Shearing Force - Chap.17), or being stretched. So reinforcing rods are particularly needed when the concrete has to withstand forces which are likely to be more than just compression.

Quartz

An important silicon compound is Quartz (silicon dioxide). If you take a small crystal of quartz and pass a tiny electric current through it, it will vibrate in a regular pattern. These regular and constant vibrations are used as the mechanism to drive quartz watches and clocks, which are noted for their accuracy and reliability.

Silicon is, of course, at the heart of the revolution in the electronics industry. Its electrical properties have enabled a vast industry to emerge and silicon 'chips' are used in almost every electrical gadget, ranging from the calculator in your pocket, the programming of washing machines to the world's most sophisticated computers. Indeed, the list is endless.

Silicates

Most of the rock-forming minerals are silicates which have combined with other elements and details of some of the main sub-groups of these are given below.

Name of Subgroup	QUARTZ	FELDSPAR	MICA	OLIVINES
COMPOSITION	Silicates	Aluminium silicate + Calcium	Hydrated Silicates	Silicates + Iron
COLOUR	Colourless	White	White to Brown	Dark Green to Black
CRYSTALLISING TEMPERAURE	Lowest ———————————————————————▶			Highest

Table 1

* This is the temperature at which minerals crystallise out of the molten magma. These minerals are all present in the Mantle and are brought to the surface as lava. Do note the rising scale of crystallising temperature, for it is the different cooling rates and crystallisation temperatures, which give rise to the great variety of rocks and minerals on the Earth's surface.

Types Of Rock

There are THREE main types of rock and the name of the type gives a clue as to how the rocks in each type were formed.

The types are:

　　　1. IGNEOUS　　2. SEDIMENTARY　　3. METAMORPHIC.

1. Igneous Rocks('Made with Fire')

These, as their name suggests, are produced from the magma which is present in the Mantle deep in the Earth. You will remember that the Mantle mainly consists of a rock called Mantle Peridotite and it is the partial melting of this which comes to the surface as the lava from volcanoes.

What Exactly Is Mantle Peridotite?

It is a complex mixture of many types of rock with each type having its own melting/crystallising temperature. An analogy with which you may be familiar is Crude Oil, which contains many hydrocarbons, each with differing properties in terms of colour, 'stickiness' (Viscosity) and flammability. The different compounds in crude oil may be separated by fractional distillation, as each compound has its own Boiling Point.

So it is with Peridotite. However, it is very difficult to analyse completely, as most of it remains in the Mantle and, in general, only part of it comes to the surface either as a form of **BASALT**, or a form of **GRANITE.**

Basalt

This is the rock which flows from the effusive volcanoes which form the ocean ridges found at constructive plate margins. It is rich in iron, which gives it its dark colour and contains all the chemicals needed (aluminium, calcium, magnesium, silicon, sodium), to produce Oceanic Crust.

As the basalts contain a higher proportion of iron and aluminium than granites (which make up the bulk of Continental Crust), this helps to explain why Oceanic Crust is denser than Continental Crust.

Another feature of basalt is its small grain size. When cooling is rapid, then only tiny crystals are formed. basalts need temperatures of over 1 000 °C to melt them, so this will be the temperature at which they erupt at the surface as a bubbling, runny (low viscosity) liquid.

Clearly, molten basalt will experience a rapid drop in temperature when it comes into contact with the surrounding air and, in particular, the waters of the oceans - thus it forms only very small crystals.

basalts return to the Mantle at destructive plate margins where they re-melt to start the cycle again.

Granite

We know granite as a hard rock used for buildings and road chippings. It seems to withstand weathering better than some of its surrounding rocks and often stands 'proud' of its surroundings as outcrops (called **Extrusions)**.

It is less dense than basalt and comes in various colours, all of which are a lighter shade than basalt. Yet, like basalt, it will have originated from the Peridotite of the Mantle. So why is it different?

A close look at the grain size, together with the fact that Granites have a much lower melting point than basalt, will give us a clue.

The large grain size will mean that the rate of cooling Granite magma is much slower, so that the crystals have time to grow. In fact, it can take many thousands of years for Granite magma to work its way to the surface - it is more viscous than basalt in the molten state.

The fact that Granitic rocks tend to be lighter in colour than basalts, indicates that Granite contains much less iron, but more silicon, than basalt. This goes a long way to explain why Granite is less dense than basalt.

The lower melting point is also a clue, as you will know that every substance has its own melting point. Thus a lower melting point than basalt indicates a different chemical composition.

Another important point is that Granites tend to be formed at destructive plate margins and because the material erupted by volcanoes at these is less dense, the Oceanic (mainly basalt) Crust, will not sink but gradually accumulates to form Continental Crust.

Where the destructive plate margins occur at an oceanic/continental boundary, the viscous granite slowly rises through the Continental rocks as pockets (called **INTRUSIONS**) of slowly cooling magma, allowing the formation and crystallisation of Granite.

Thus, Granitic Continental Crust does not return to the Mantle (unlike basalt), but gradually increases at the Earth's surface - and adds to the land mass.

2. Sedimentary Rocks

These, as their name suggests, are formed when igneous rocks are broken up into small pieces and are deposited as layers (STRATA).

The breaking up process is called WEATHERING and this falls into two distinctive types:
    i) **Physical weathering** - mechanical break-up of the rocks;
    ii) **Chemical weathering** - chemical decomposition of the rocks.

How Does Physical Weathering Take Place?

1) Action Of Frost:

Water may seep into small cracks in the rocks and then freeze. As water expands when it freezes, the ice widens the crack in the rock. This process is repeated until the crack is so wide that the rock breaks. It may fall down a mountainside breaking up further as it falls, or break bits off other rocks during its descent.

2) Isostatic Uplift:

a) It is known that ice age rocks have less pressure on them now.

b) A weathered surface has less mass. This causes a pressure release from below and new rocks rise to be weathered.

3. Temporal Changes

a) In deserts there is a large temperature difference between night and day. This means that rocks will expand during the day (when temperatures are higher than the night temperatures) and contract during the very cold nights. This constant expansion and contraction creates immense pressures in the rocks which lead them to crack and crumble.

b) Different minerals will heat up or cool down faster (e.g. mica and felspar in granite). This will also put a strain in the rocks resulting in crumbling.

Chemical Weathering

The carbon dioxide in the air dissolves in the rain to make it slightly acid. This acid will attack some of the compounds in the rocks and one of three things could happen:

1. The soluble products produced from the action of weak acid on the rock could be carried away into the sea by rivers.

2. The insoluble residues remaining are now different rocks.

3. Part of the rock is not affected by chemical weathering.

In the cases of (2) and (3), what remains are called RESIDUAL MINERALS.

Erosion

The products of weathering are now moved away from the initial rock by various methods. They could be blown by the wind, be carried by running water, or just fall. The removal of matter makes the initial rock smaller and this part of the rock cycle is called **EROSION**.

Transportation and Deposition

The matter removed by weathering is transported by anything that can move the particles. Evidence from the glaciers shows that ice will push huge amounts of matter along. In Britain, by far the most common method of transportation is by water. Rocks and pebbles, as they are carried along by moving water, crash against the sides and bed of the river thus causing erosion. This process is a type of erosion called **Abrasion** (or sometimes, **Corrasion**). Even the stones themselves crash into each other and break into smaller bits - this is known as **Attrition**.

Water flowing down a hillside will have enough energy to move fairly large boulders. As the river flows, it uses its energy to (a) transport materials and (b) erode the river bank - and so it begins to slow down. At this point, the larger particles are DEPOSITED and it is only the smaller particles which are carried along in SUSPENSION until the flow of the river is so slow that the particles are deposited as SEDIMENTS.

These sediments build up in layers (STRATA) with the lower layers becoming more compressed as further layers are deposited on top. Eventually, the lower layers will bind together as a SEDIMENTARY ROCK. Sandstone is a good example of a sedimentary rock, as is Limestone.

How Is Limestone Formed?

This is formed in oceans from the shell of many marine animals. When the animal dies, the shell (made of calcium carbonate) falls to the sea bed and when there is an abundance of these shells, limestone is formed layer by layer.

The fact that Britain has large quantities of limestone on the land, shows that at one time, what is now land, was once part of the continental shelf of an ocean.

Metamorphic Rocks

(Metamorphosis - A Complete Change Of Form)

Deep underground, the action of heat or pressure, or both, will completely change sedimentary rocks into something which is usually harder. This is rather like pottery clay which, when 'fired' in a kiln, becomes harder.

The main thing to remember is that the chemical composition does not alter (think of making toast).

What **does** change is the crystallisation, and hence formation, of different minerals in the rock which, as we have seen earlier, takes place at different temperatures. The new crystals which grow, appear in the rock as speckles and it is this speckly appearance which is so characteristic of metamorphic rocks.

A good example of this is Marble, which is the metamorphic version of limestone. The speckles and veins can be clearly seen and the fact that marble is much harder than limestone makes it a popular, but expensive, choice for use in building.

In some places, the sedimentary rocks are brought to high enough temperatures to melt them, producing magmas which are similar in composition to Granite.

So the Rock Cycle is now complete.

The Rock Cycle

1. Molten magma works its way to the surface, cooling slowly as granite intrusions.

2. At the surface, weathering (Physical/Chemical) followed by: erosion, transportation and sedimentation lead to the formation in layers (Strata) of Sedimentary rocks.

3. Sedimentary rocks become buried by other layers and/or plate activity until, deep in the hot interior of the Crust, the action of heat and pressure cause them to be 'baked' with different minerals being formed, thus changing them into Metamorphic rocks.

Fig 19.1 The Rock Cycle

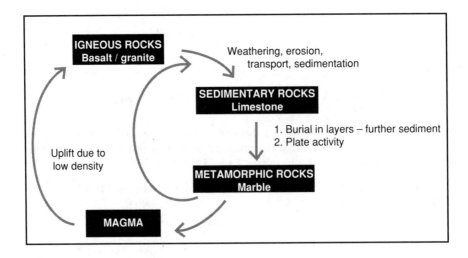

4. Some metamorphic rocks work their way to the surface to begin the weathering cycle once more. Others go deeper and form part of the magma from which new granite is made.

What Do You Know About Rocks?

1. (a) Name the three main Rock types found in the Earth's Crust.
    (b) Say, briefly, how each type is formed.

2. Explain what is meant by the following terms from the Rock Cycle:
    i) Physical weathering,   ii) Chemical weathering,
    iii) Erosion,   iv) Transportation,
    v) Sediment.

3. What is a mineral?

4. What is the name given to the study of rocks?

5. Which two elements make up 75% of the Earth's Crust?

6. What does the word STRATA describe?

7. (i) What is it that affects the grain size of rocks?
    (ii)Which has the larger grain size, Basalt or Granite? Give a reason.

8. Which rock is the main part of Oceanic Crust?

9. What is the metamorphic form of limestone?

10. How was limestone formed in the first place?

11. Give three uses which we make of sand.

12. What is reinforced concrete?

Further Questions On Rocks

Use the following information and Table 1 in this chapter, to help you answer question 1.

i) Basalts melt at around 1 100°C., whereas Granites melt at around 800°C.

ii)Granites contain about 60% Feldspars but no Olivines;

Basalts contain No Feldspars but over 80% Olivines.

iii)Basalts and Granite both originate from Mantle Peridotite.

1.   a) Where on the Earth's surface do Basalts and Granites emerge?

b) Make sensible comments about the reasons for the differing amounts of Olivines in Basalt and Granite, even though they originate from the same material.

c) Comment on the respective colouring of Basalt and Granite.

2.   Give as much detail as you can about the Rock Cycle, with particular reference to Granite.

3.   Erosion of rocks results in small particles being deposited as sediments. Some of the sediments stay as sand, whilst others form fertile soil. Explain, as fully as you can, the differences between infertile sand and fertile soil.

4.   If you were going to 'reclaim' part of the Sahara Desert to enable crops to grow, what steps would you take to achieve this and what problems would you have to overcome?

5.   You have been asked to design a Multi-Storey car park with three floors. Remember that reinforced concrete is an expensive, but for some uses, a necessary material.

Draw a side view (elevation) of such a building, showing the most economical, but safest construction.

Index